Laboratory Manual

D1517858

Author

Morris Hein

ISBN 9781119050391

Printed in the United States of America 10 9 8 7 6 5 4 3 2 1

List of Titles

Introduction to General, Organic, and Biochemistry in the Laboratory, 10th edition

by Morris Hein, Judith N. Peisen, and James M. Ritchey
Copyright © 2012, ISBN: 978-0-470-59881-8

Table of Contents

Preface

This manual is intended for the student with little or no previous coursework in chemistry who is usually enrolled in a two-semester chemistry sequence for non-majors, often preparing for careers in allied health programs such as nursing, radiography, medical lab technician, etc. The experiments begin with very simple laboratory techniques, measurements, physical and chemical properties, and calculations needed by beginning students in a foundations course and progress to relatively complex procedures typical of General Chemistry students. The last sixteen experiments provide a sequence of organic chemistry and biochemistry experiments. The number and variety of experiments provide the instructor with reasonable flexibility in preparing a laboratory schedule to support and complement the course lecture topics for students of varying previous experience with chemistry.

Our major objectives of this flexible laboratory program are to provide experience with (1) hands-on laboratory experimentation, (2) the capabilities and limitations of measurements, (3) a variety of chemical reactions and the equations used to describe them, (4) the collection, analysis, and graphing of data, (5) responsible disposal of chemicals for personal and environmental health, (6) Using a computer for graphing of data, (7) drawing valid conclusions from experimental evidence, and (8) support and reinforcement of concepts introduced in the lecture component of the course.

We have tried to maintain a balance between descriptive and quantitative experiments at all levels of a non-majors course (introductory, general chem., organic/biochem). Nine experiments provide experience with physical properties of matter; ten experiments include unknowns for student analysis, and nine provide opportunities for graphing data. All experiments emphasize basic skills and data analysis. The instructor's manual provides sample student data, including graphs, for most experiments.

The format is designed to be helpful and convenient for both student and instructor and includes the following features:

1. A concise discussion of the basic underlying principles for each experiment provides pertinent background material to supplement, not replace, the textbook.

2. Six Study Aids provide supplementary material common to several experiments on the important topics of (a) significant figures, (b) chemical formulas and equations, (c) reading and preparing graphs by hand and by computer, (d) use of a scientific calculator, (e) Dimensional Analysis and Stoichiometry, and (f) introduction to organic chemistry.

3. Experimental procedures have been extensively tested by many students and provide enough detail for students to work with only general supervision.

4. Report forms for each experiment are cross-referenced to letters and subtitles in the procedure, designed to be completed before leaving the lab session, and relatively easy to grade.

5. The names and formulas of reagents used are listed at the beginning of each experiment.

6. Special safety precautions and waste disposal instructions are indicated when necessary at the point where they are required within the procedure.

7. For the convenience of the instructor and stockroom personnel, the appendices provide (a) an experiment-by-experiment list of special equipment and preparations needed, (b) a list of suggested equipment for student lockers, (c) an experiment-by-experiment list of waste disposal instructions, (d) a list of suggested auxiliary equipment, and (e) a complete list of reagents and details for the preparation of solutions.

8. The lab manual also contains 26 Exercises, many of which can be used as supplements for a number of experiments. Exercises 25 and 26 (Molecular Models and Isomerism and Stereoisomerism—Optical Activity) may be used as experiments to give students hands-on experience in these subjects.

The experiment which is new to the Tenth Edition is Experiment 8, Water, Solutions, and pH. This experiment provides an introduction to the properties of water especially important in the life sciences, introduces some skills used in biotechnology and the concept of molarity. This new experiment is an excellent foundation for Experiment 9, Properties of Solutions which is found in previous editions. Properties of Lead (II), Silver, and Mercury (I) Ions (Experiment 14 in the twelfth edition) which involved the use of heavy metal cations, has been eliminated.

Meticulous instructions for waste disposal have been continued and updated for students within each procedure and in the Instructor's Manual. The instructions for Preparing a Graph (Study Aid 3) have been updated to the most recent version of Excel (2007).

We are especially indebted to students in the chemistry departments of Mount San Antonio College and Hagerstown Community College for their patience and helpful suggestions during the development and testing of this laboratory program. We appreciate the feedback from instructors and students at the many schools over the years that have used this lab manual in their introductory chemistry course. A special thanks to Dr. Richard Montgomery, Dr. William Elliott, and Dr. Melanie Ulrich for their contribution to the Water, Solutions, and pH experiment that is new to this edition. Further suggestions for improvements of material in this laboratory manual are always welcome.

Morris Hein
Judith N. Peisen
James M. Ritchey

To the Student

Since your laboratory time is limited, it is important to come to each session prepared by at least one hour of detailed study of the scheduled experiment. This should be considered a standing homework assignment.

Each of the experiments in this manual is composed of four parts:

1. **Materials and Equipment**—a list that includes the formulas of all substances used in each experiment.

2. **Discussion**—a brief discussion of the principles underlying the experiment.

3. **Procedure**—detailed directions for performing the experiment with safety precautions clearly noted and disposal procedures for chemical waste provided throughout and identified by a waste icon.

4. **Report for Experiment**—a form for recording data and observations, performing calculations, and answering questions.

Follow the directions in the procedure carefully, and consult your instructor if you have any questions. For convenience, the letters and subtitles in the report form have been set up to correspond with those in the procedure section of each experiment.

As you make your observations and obtain your data, record them on the report form. Try to use your time efficiently; when a reaction or process is occurring that takes considerable time and requires little watching, start working on other parts of the experiment, perform calculations, answer questions on the report form, or clean up your equipment.

Except when your instructor directs otherwise, you should do all the work individually. You may profit by discussing experimental results with your classmates, but in the final analysis you must rely on your own observations and judgment in completing the report form.

⚠ Safety Guidelines

While in the chemistry laboratory, you are responsible not only for your own safety but for the safety of everyone else. *We have included safety precautions in every experiment where needed, and they are highlighted with the icon shown in the title of this section.* Your instructor may modify these instructions and give you more specific directions on safety in your laboratory. If the proper precautions and techniques are used, none of the experiments in this laboratory program are hazardous. But without your reading and following the instructions, without knowledge about handling and disposal of chemicals, and without the use of common sense at all times, accidents can happen. Even when everyone is doing his or her best to comply with the safety guidelines in each experiment, accidents can happen. It is your responsibility to minimize these accidents and know what to do if they happen.

Laboratory Rules and Safety Procedures

1. **Wear protective goggles or glasses** at all times in the laboratory work area. These glasses should wrap around the face so liquids cannot splash into the eye from the side. These goggles are mandated by eye-protection laws and are not optional, even though they may be uncomfortable. Contact lenses increase the risk of problems with eye safety, even when protective goggles are worn. If you wear contact lenses, inform the instructor.

2. **Dress appropriately** for the laboratory. Shoes that do not completely cover the feet are not allowed *(no sandals)*. Long hair should be tied back. Wear a laboratory coat or apron, if available, to protect your clothing.

3. **Keep your benchtop organized as you work.** Put jackets, book bags, and personal belongings away from the work areas. Before you leave, clean your work area and make sure the gas and water are turned off. Clean and return all glassware and equipment to your drawer or the lab bench where you borrowed it.

4. **Keep all stock bottles of solid and liquid reagents in the dispensing area.** Do not bring reagent bottles to your laboratory work area. Use test tubes, beakers, or weigh boats to obtain chemicals from the dispensing areas: (1) the reagent shelf, (2) the balance tables, (3) under the fume hood, and (4) as instructed.

5. **Keep the balance and the area around it clean.** Do not place chemicals directly on the balance pans; place a piece of weighing paper, a weigh boat, or another small container on the pan first, and then weigh your material. **Never weigh an object while it is hot.**

6. **Check the labels on every reagent bottle carefully.** Many names and formulas appear similar at first glance. Label every beaker, test tube, etc., into which you transfer chemicals. Many labels will contain the National Fire Protection Association (NFPA) diamond label, which provides information about the flammability, reactivity, health effects, and miscellaneous effects for the substance. Each hazard is rated 0 (least hazardous) to 4 (most hazardous). For example, the NFPA label for potassium chromate is shown below.

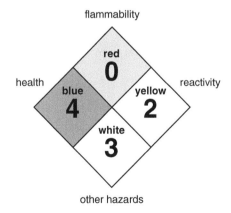

More specific information (the reason for potassium chromate being rated an extreme health hazard, for example) about all known substances is available in the form of Material Safety Data Sheets (MSDS), which many institutions keep on file for chemicals stored and used in their laboratories. MSDSs are usually provided with chemicals by the supplier when they are purchased and are easily obtained from many website sources. Because of its hazardous nature, chromates have been removed from this lab manual.

7. **Never return unused chemicals to the reagent bottles.** This is a source of possible contamination of the entire stock bottle. Dispose of unused chemicals exactly as instructed in the waste disposal instructions for that substance, identified by WASTE DISPOSE OF PROPERLY throughout each experiment.

8. **Disposal of wastes must follow state and federal guidelines.** Do not put anything into the trash or sink without thinking first. We have tried to anticipate every disposal decision in the procedure and marked the procedure with the waste icon. The following guidelines are the foundation of waste disposal decisions:

    a. Broken glass is put into a clearly marked special container.

    b. Organic solvents are never poured into the sink. They are usually flammable and often immiscible with water. Instead, they are poured into a specially marked container ("waste organic solvents") provided when needed.

    c. Solutions containing cations and anions considered toxic by the EPA are never poured into the sink. They are poured into specially marked containers ("waste heavy metal," etc.) provided when needed. The name of all ions disposed of into a specific bottle must be listed on the label.

    d. Solutions poured in the sink should be washed down with plenty of water.

    e. Some solid chemicals must also be disposed of in specially labeled containers. If you are not sure what to do, ask the instructor.

    f. Each school may have its own policy for waste disposal which supercedes the instructions in this manual.

9. **Avoid contaminating stock solutions.** Do not insert medicine droppers or pipets into reagent bottles containing liquids. Instead, pour a little of the liquid into a small beaker or test tube. If the bottle is fitted with a special pipet that is stored with the bottle, this may not be necessary.

10. **Avoid all direct contact with chemicals.**

    a. Wash your hands anytime you get chemicals on them and at the end of the laboratory session.

    b. If you spill something, clean it up immediately before it dries or gets on your papers or skin.

    c. **Never** pipet by mouth.

    d. **Never** eat, drink, or smoke in the laboratory.

    e. Do not look down into the open end of a test tube in which a reaction is being conducted, and do not point the open end of a test tube at someone else.

    f. Inhale odors and chemicals with great caution. Waft vapors toward your nose. The fume hood will be used for all irritating and toxic vapors.

11. **Working with glass requires special precautions:**

    a. Do not heat graduated cylinders, burets, pipets, or bottles with a burner flame.

    b. Do not hold a test tube or beaker in your hand during a chemical reaction.

– x –

c. Do not touch glass that has been near a flame or hot plate. Hot glass looks the same as cool glass and may cause serious burns.

d. Learn and practice proper procedures when inserting glass tubing into rubber stoppers. (See Experiment 1)

12. **Learn the location and proper use of safety equipment:** fire extinguisher, eye wash, first aid kit, fire blanket, safety shower, spill kits, and other equipment available.

13. **Never work alone** in the laboratory area.

14. **Report all accidents** to the instructor, no matter how minor.

15. **Do not perform unauthorized experiments.**

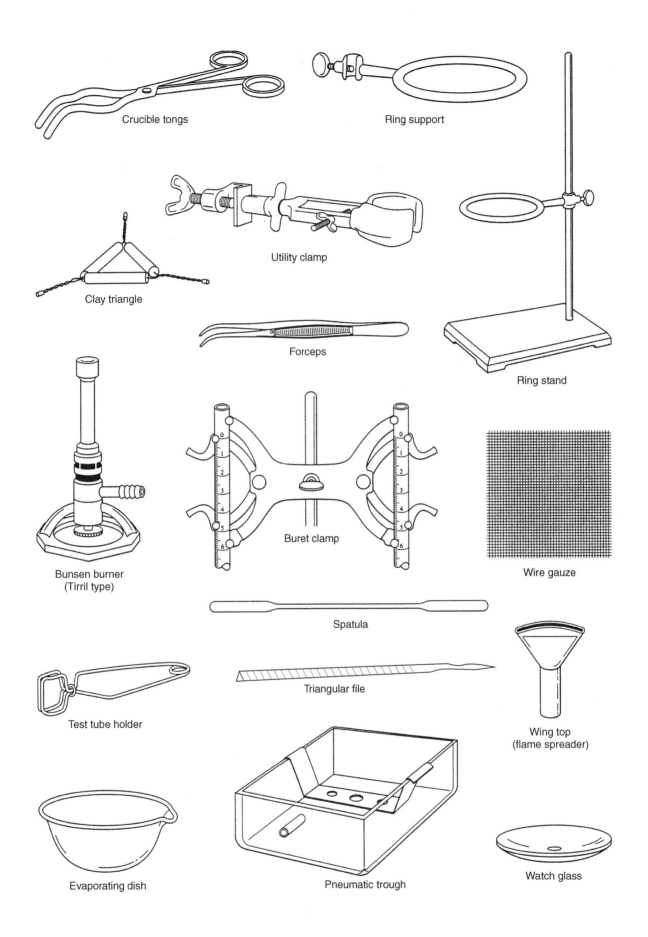

Crucible tongs

Ring support

Utility clamp

Clay triangle

Forceps

Ring stand

Bunsen burner
(Tirril type)

Buret clamp

Wire gauze

Spatula

Test tube holder

Triangular file

Wing top
(flame spreader)

Evaporating dish

Pneumatic trough

Watch glass

– xii –

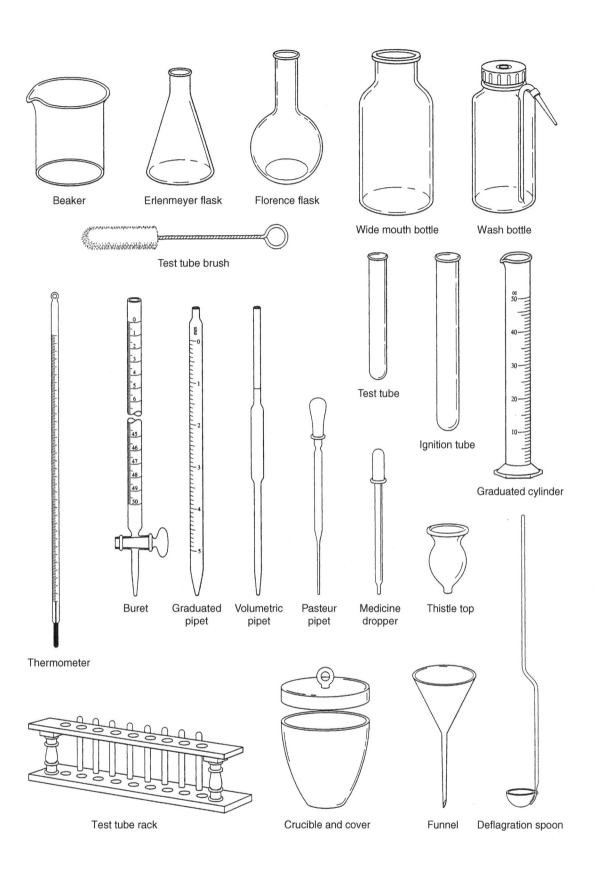

Beaker

Erlenmeyer flask

Florence flask

Wide mouth bottle

Wash bottle

Test tube brush

Test tube

Ignition tube

Graduated cylinder

Thermometer

Buret

Graduated pipet

Volumetric pipet

Pasteur pipet

Medicine dropper

Thistle top

Test tube rack

Crucible and cover

Funnel

Deflagration spoon

Experiment 1   Physical and Chemical Changes & the

Conservation Of Mass

I. Physical Changes

A physical change is any change NOT involving a change in the substance's chemical identity. Here are some examples:

(1) any phase change. Moving between solid, liquid and gas involves only the amount of energy in the sample (this amount is the subject of future lessons). There is no effect on the chemical identity of the substance. For example, water remains water, no matter if it is a solid, liquid or gas: $H_2O_{(s)}$ (ice) $\rightarrow$ $H_2O_{(L)}$ (liquid water)

(2) grinding something into a powder. Or the reverse process of making a bigger lump of stuff, say by melting lots of small pellets of copper into one big piece.

(3) iron (and other metals) can be made to be magnetic. This change in no way affects the chemical identity of the element. Iron that is magnetized rusts just as easily as iron that is not magnetized.

Now would be a good time as any to list the names of the various phase changes:

Change	Name of Change
Solid to Liquid	Melting, fusion
Liquid to Gas	Boiling, evaporation
Solid to Gas	Sublimation
Gas to Solid	Deposition
Gas to Liquid	Condensation, liquefaction
Liquid to Solid	Freezing, solidification

An example of sublimation is dry ice. It is solid carbon dioxide and goes directly from the solid state to gas in the open atmosphere. You can make liquid carbon dioxide, but it must be done under about 5 atmospheres of pressure.

Deposition is a bit of a non-standard word, but it fits better than using sublimation or condensation again. Ice cubes in the freezer undergo sublimation to water vapor, even when the ice is cold. The water vapor deposits back onto the solid ice without even going through the liquid phase. By the way, this is how ice cubes become "welded" together if they sit undisturbed in the freezer.

II. Chemical Changes

A "chemical change" means that the reacting substance(s) are changed into new substances. The actual atoms involved remain, they are simply rearranged. The rearrangement is called a chemical reaction. For example:

$$2H_2O ---> 2H_2 + O_2$$

is a chemical reaction in which water is broken down into the elements, hydrogen and oxygen, which make it up. Notice how the amounts of hydrogen atoms (four) and oxygen atoms (two) do not change from one side of the arrow to the other. However, the arrangements of the atoms are different. Some chemical bonds (the one involved in the water) have been broken and some new chemical bonds (the ones in hydrogen and oxygen) have been formed. This is another way to define "chemical change:" A process in which chemical bonds are broken and new ones are made. A process like grinding some salt crystals into a fine powder does not involve the breaking of chemical bonds and the formation of new ones, so it is a physical change. Obviously, chemistry is made up of many chemical changes. One interesting one is the ion-exchange column which is used to remove certain chemicals from drinking water.

Law of Conservation of Mass
Probably the best-known and most widely accepted of the empirical laws known to Dalton was the **law of conservation of (total) mass**, which had been used by the French chemist Antoine L. Lavoisier in 1798. It was probably first assumed, then verified by a few crude experiments, because it can only be truly verified by very precise experiments using sealed systems. These precise experiments were carried out some fifty to one hundred years later. It had generally been accepted by scientists, however, even prior to the work of Lavoisier. The law of conservation of mass can be stated as follows: **The total mass of the reactants in any chemical reaction is exactly equal to
the total mass of the products.**

EQUIPMENT
bunsen burner, dropper pipette, 5 test tubes (18x150-mm), mortar and pestle, test tube rack, magnet, test tube holder, watch glass, safety goggles, evaporating dish, 50 mL beakers.
MATERIALS
copper sulfate pentahydrate ($CuSO_4$ 5 H_2O), magnesium ribbon (Mg), sodium chloride (NaCl), paper (5 cm x 10 cm), candle, silver nitrate (0.1 M $AgNO_3$), matches, 0.5 M solutions of NaOH, $CuSO_4$, NH_4OH, 1.0 M HCl, and Na_2CO_3

SAFETY
When heating a substance in a test tube, be sure the open end of the tube points away from yourself and others.
Handle all acids with extra caution. Always wear safety goggles . Report all acid spills to your instrucrtor, and flush with cold water.
Give a heated glass sample time to cool before handling it. Glass retains heat. Tie back long hair and secure loose clothing before working. Wear safety goggles at all times when working in the lab.

EXPERIMENT 2

Measurements

MATERIALS AND EQUIPMENT

Solids: sodium chloride (NaCl) and ice. Balance, ruler, thermometer, solid object for density determination, No. 1 or 2 solid rubber stopper.

DISCUSSION

Chemistry is an experimental science, and measurements are fundamental to most of the experiments. It is important to learn how to make and use these measurements properly.

The SI System of Units

The International System of Units (*Systeme Internationale, SI*) or metric system is a decimal system of units for measurements used almost exclusively in science. It is built around a set of units including the meter, the gram, and the liter and uses factors of 10 to express larger or smaller multiples of these units. To express larger or smaller units, prefixes are added to the names of the units. Deci, centi, and milli are units that are 1/10, 1/100, and 1/1000, respectively, of these units. The most common of these prefixes with their corresponding values expressed as decimals and powers of 10 are shown in the table below.

Prefix	Decimal Equivalent	Power of 10	Examples
deci (d)	0.1	10^{-1}	1 dg = 0.1 g = 10^{-1} g
centi (c)	0.01	10^{-2}	1 cm = 0.01 m = 10^{-2} m
milli (m)	0.001	10^{-3}	1 mg = 0.001 g = 10^{-3} g
kilo (k)	1000	10^{3}	1 km = 1000 m = 10^{3} m

Dimensional Analysis

It will often be necessary to convert from the American System of units to the SI system or to convert units within the SI system. Conversion factors are available from tables (see Appendix 4) or can be developed from the metric prefixes and their corresponding values as shown in the table above. Dimensional analysis, a problem-solving method with many applications in chemistry, is very valuable for converting one unit to another by the use of conversion factors. A review of using dimensional analysis for converting units is provided here. Study Aid 5 provides more help with this problem-solving tool.

Conversion Factors come from equivalent relationships, usually stated as equations. From each equivalence statement two conversion factors can be written in fractional form with a value of 1. For example:

Equivalence Equations	Conversion Factor #1	Conversion Factor #2
1 dollar = 4 quarters	$\dfrac{1 \text{ dollar}}{4 \text{ quarters}}$	$\dfrac{4 \text{ quarters}}{1 \text{ dollar}}$
1 lb = 453.6 g	$\dfrac{1 \text{ lb}}{453.6 \text{ g}}$	$\dfrac{453.6 \text{ g}}{1 \text{ lb}}$
1 mm = 10^{-3} m	$\dfrac{1 \text{ mm}}{10^{-3}\text{m}}$	$\dfrac{10^{-3}\text{m}}{1 \text{ mm}}$
1 ns = 10^{-9} s	$\dfrac{1 \text{ ns}}{10^{-9}\text{s}}$	$\dfrac{10^{-9}\text{s}}{1 \text{ ns}}$

The dimensional analysis method of converting units involves organizing one or more conversion factors into a logical series which cancels or eliminates all units except the unit(s) wanted in the answer.

For example: To convert 2.53 lb into milligrams (mg), the setup is:

$$(2.53 \text{ lb})\left(\frac{453.6 \text{ g}}{1 \text{ lb}}\right)\left(\frac{1 \text{ mg}}{10^{-3}\text{g}}\right) = 1.15 \times 10^6 \text{ mg}$$

Note, that in completing this calculation, units are treated as numbers, **lb** in the denominator is canceled into **lb** in the numerator and **g** in the denominator is cancelled into **g** in the numerator. More examples of unit conversions can be found in Study Aid 5.

Although the SI unit of temperature is the Kelvin (K), the Celsius (or centigrade) temperature scale is commonly used in scientific work and the Fahrenheit scale is commonly used in this country. On the Celsius scale the freezing point of water is designated 0°C, the boiling point 100°C.

Precision and Accuracy of Measurements

Scientific measurements must be as **precise** as possible. This means that every measurement will include one uncertain or estimated digit. When making measurements we normally estimate between the smallest scale divisions on the instrument being used. Then, only the uncertain digit should vary if the measurement is repeated using the same instrument, even if it is repeated by someone else. The **accuracy** of a measurement or calculated quantity refers to its agreement with some known value. For example, we need to make two measurements, volume and mass, to determine the density of a metal. This experimental density can then be compared with the density of the metal listed in a reference such as the *Handbook of Chemistry and Physics*. High accuracy means there is good agreement between the experimental value and the known value listed in the reference. Not all measurements can be compared with a known value.

Random and Systematic Errors

The difference between the experimentally measured value of something and the accepted value of something is known as **the error.** For many of the experiments in this course, after you determine the error in your result, you may be required to find the percent error:

$$\text{Percent error} = \frac{\text{theoretical accepted value} - \text{experimentally determined value}}{\text{theoretical accepted value}} \times 100$$

There are two different types of error. **A random error** means that the error has an equal probablilty of being higher or lower than the accepted value. For example, a student measures the density of a quartz sample four times: (Accepted density value for quartz is 2.65 g/mL)

2.72 g/mL
2.55 g/mL Since two of the measured density values are below the mean
2.68 g/mL and two are above the mean, there is an **equal probability** of the
2.60 g/mL measurements being above or below the mean. This is a **random** error.
Since the mean density value is very close to the accepted value, the
Mean = 2.64 g/mL accuracy of the mean measurement is good. (the percent error is 0.38%)

The other type of error is a **systematic error.** This type of error occurs in the same direction each time (either always higher or always lower than the accepted value). For example, a student measures the boiling point of water four times (accepted temperature for the boiling point of water is 100.0° C.)

101.2° C
100.9° C Since all four of the measured temperature values are above the accepted
102.0° C value, the **error** is systematic. The mean value is 1.3% higher than the
101.0° C accepted value so the accuracy of these measurements is not as good as the
Mean = 101.3° C accuracy of the density of the measurements in the first example.

Precision and Significant Figures

When a measured value is determined to the highest precision of the measuring instrument, the digits in the measurement are called **significant digits** or **significant figures.**

Suppose we are measuring two pieces of wire, using the metric scale on a ruler that is calibrated in tenths of centimeters as shown in Figures 2.1a and b. One end of the first wire is placed at exactly 0.0 cm and the other end falls somewhere between 6.3 cm and 6.4 cm. Since the distance between 6.3 and 6.4 is very small, it is difficult to determine the next digit exactly. One person might estimate the length of the wire as 6.34 cm and another as 6.33 cm. The estimated digit is never ignored because it tells us that the ruler can be read to the 0.01 place. This measurement therefore has three significant figures (two certain and one uncertain figure).

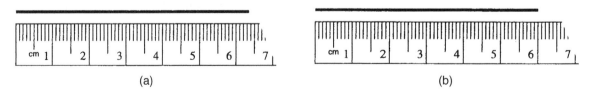

(a)   (b)

Figure 2.1

The second wire has a length which measures exactly 6 cm on the ruler as shown in Figure 2.1b. Reporting this length as 6 cm would be a mistake for it would imply that the 6 is an uncertain digit and others might record 5 or 7 as the measurement. Recording the measurement as 6.0 would also be incorrect because it implies that the 0 is uncertain and that someone else might estimate the length as 6.1 or 5.9. What we really mean is that, as closely as we can read it, the length is exactly 6 cm. So, we must write the number in such a way that it tells how precisely we can read it. In this example we can estimate to 0.01 cm so the length should be reported as 6.00 cm.

Significant Figures in Calculations

The result of multiplication, division, or other mathematical manipulation cannot be more precise than the least precise measurement used in the calculation. For instance, suppose we have an object that weighs 3.62 lb and we want to calculate the mass in grams. $(3.62 \text{ lb})\left(\dfrac{453.6 \text{ g}}{1 \text{ lb}}\right) = 1{,}642.032$ when done by a calculator. To report 1,642.032 g as the mass is absurd, for it implies a precision far beyond that of the original measurement. Although the conversion factor has four significant figures, the mass in pounds has only three significant figures. Therefore the answer should have only three significant figures; that is, 1,640 g. In this case the zero cannot be considered significant. This value can be more properly expressed as 1.64×10^3g. For a more comprehensive discussion of significant figures see Study Aid 1.

Precise Quantities versus Approximate Quantities

In conducting an experiment it is often unnecessary to measure an exact quantity of material. For instance, the directions might state, "Weigh about 2 g of sodium sulfite." This instruction indicates that the measured quantity of salt should be 2 g plus or minus a small quantity. In this example 1.8 to 2.2 g will satisfy these requirements. To weigh exactly 2.00 g or 2.000 g wastes time since the directions call for approximately 2 g.

Sometimes it is necessary to measure an amount of material precisely within a stated quantity range. Suppose the directions read, "weigh about 2 g of sodium sulfite to the nearest 0.001 g." This instruction does not imply that the amount is 2.000 g but that it should be between 1.8 and 2.2 g and measured and recorded to three decimal places. Therefore, four different students might weigh their samples and obtain 2.141 g, 2.034 g, 1.812 g, and 1.937 g, respectively, and each would have satisfactorily followed the directions.

Temperature

The simple act of measuring a temperature with a thermometer can easily involve errors. Not only does the calibration of the scale on the thermometer limit the precision of the measurement, but the improper placement of the thermometer bulb in the material being measured introduces a common source of human error. When measuring the temperature of a liquid, one can minimize this type of error by observing the following procedures:

1. Hold the thermometer away from the walls of the container.

2. Allow sufficient time for the thermometer to reach equilibrium with the liquid.

3. Be sure the liquid is adequately mixed.

When converting from degrees Celsius to Fahrenheit or vice versa, we make use of the following formulas:

$$°C = \frac{(°F - 32)}{1.8} \text{ or } °F = (1.8 \times °C) + 32$$

Example Problem: Convert 70.0°F to degrees Celsius:

$$°C = \left(\frac{70.0°F - 32}{1.8} \right) = \frac{38.0}{1.8} = 21.11°C \text{ rounded to } 21.1°C$$

This example shows not only how the formula is used but also a typical setup of the way chemistry problems should be written. It shows how the numbers are used, but does not show the multiplication and division, which should be worked out by calculator. The answer was changed from 21.11°C to 21.1°C because the initial temperature, 70.0°F, has only three significant figures. The 1.8 and 32 in the formulas are exact numbers and have no effect on the number of significant figures.

Mass (Weight)

The directions in this manual are written for a 0.001 gram precision balance, but all the experiments can be performed satisfactorily using a 0.01 gram or 0.0001 gram precision balance. Your instructor will give specific directions on how to use the balance, but the following precautions should be observed:

1. The balance should always be "zeroed" before anything is placed on the balance pan. On an electronic digital balance, this is done with the "tare" or "T" button. Balances without this feature should be adjusted by the instructor.

2. Never place chemicals directly on the balance pan; first place them on a weighing paper, weighing "boat", or in a container. Clean up any materials you spill on or around the balance.

3. Before moving objects on and off the pan, be sure the balance is in the "arrest" position. When you leave the balance, return the balance to the "arrest" or standby position.

4. Never try to make adjustments on a balance. If it seems out of order, tell your instructor.

Volume

Beakers and flasks are marked to indicate only approximate volumes. Volume measurements are therefore made in a graduated cylinder by reading the point on the graduated scale that coincides with the bottom of the curved surface called the **meniscus** of the liquid (Figure 2.2). Volumes measured in this illustrated graduated cylinder are calibrated in 1 mL increments and should be estimated and recorded to the nearest 0.1 mL.

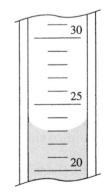

Figure 2.2 Read the bottom of the meniscus. The volume is 23.0 mL

Density

Density is a physical property of a substance and is useful in identifying the substance. **Density** is the ratio of the mass of a substance to the volume occupied by that mass; it is the mass per unit volume and is given by the equations

$$\text{Density} = d = \frac{\text{Mass}}{\text{Volume}} = \frac{m}{V} = \frac{g}{mL} \text{ or } \frac{g}{cm^3}$$

In calculating density it is important to make correct use of units and mathematical setups.

Example Problem: An object weighs 283.5 g and occupies a volume of 14.6 mL. What is its density?

$$d = \frac{m}{V} = \frac{283.5 \text{ g}}{14.6 \text{ mL}} = 19.4 \text{ g/mL}$$

Note that all the operations involved in the calculation are properly indicated and that all units are shown. If we divide grams by milliliters, we get an answer in grams per milliliter.

The volume of an irregularly shaped object is usually measured by the displacement of a liquid. An object completely submerged in a liquid displaces a volume of the liquid equal to the volume of the object.

Measurement data and calculations must always be accompanied by appropriate units.

PROCEDURE

Wear protective glasses.

Record your data on the report form as you complete each measurement, never on a scrap of paper which can be lost or misplaced.

A. Temperature

Record all temperatures to the **nearest 0.1°C.**   water room temperature: 21.9°C .

DEMO 1. Fill a 400 mL beaker half full of tap water. Place your thermometer in the beaker. Give it a minute to reach thermal equilibrium. Keeping the thermometer in the water and holding the tip of the thermometer away from the glass, read and record the temperature.

skip 2. Fill a 150 mL beaker half full of tap water. Set up a ring stand with the ring and wire gauze at a height so the hottest part of the burner flame will reach the bottom of the beaker. Heat the water to boiling. Read and record the temperature of the boiling water, being sure to hold the thermometer away from the bottom of the beaker.

3. Fill a 250 mL beaker one-fourth full of tap water and add a 100 mL beaker of crushed ice. Without stirring, place the thermometer in the beaker, resting it on the bottom. Wait at least 1 minute, then read and record the temperature. Now stir the mixture for about 1 minute. If almost all the ice melts, add more. Holding the thermometer off the bottom, read and record the temperature. Save the ice-water mixture for Part 4.   1.9 .

skip 4. Weigh approximately 5 g of sodium chloride and add it to the ice-water mixture. Stir for 1 minute, adding more ice if needed. Read and record the temperature. Dispose of the salt water/ice mixture in the sink.

WASTE
DISPOSE OF
PROPERLY

B. Mass

Using the balance provided, do the following, recording all the masses to include one uncertain digit and all certain digits.

DEMO 1. Weigh a 250 mL beaker.   107.860

skip 2. Weigh a 125 mL Erlenmeyer flask.

3. Weigh a piece of weighing paper or a plastic weighing "boat."   2.111 g

4. Add approximately 2 g of sodium chloride to the weighing paper from step 3 and record the total mass. Calculate the mass of sodium chloride.   4.103 g .

C. Length

Using a ruler, make the following measurements in centimeters; measure to the nearest uncertain digit.

1. Measure the length of the arrow on the right   ⟶   5.30 cm.

DEMO 2. Measure the external height of a 250 mL beaker.   8.90 cm
    use 2 decimal places on the ruler

3. Measure the length of a test tube.   14.69 cm .

D. Volume

Using the graduated cylinder most appropriate, measure the following volumes to the maximum precision possible, usually 0.1 mL. Remember to read the volume at the meniscus.

DEMO 1. Fill a test tube to the brim with water and measure the volume of the water. 30.1 mL

2. Fill a 125 mL Erlenmeyer flask to the brim with water and measure the volume of the water. 151.1 mL.   2 mL > 1.1 mL   1 mL

skip 3. Measure 5.0 mL of water in a graduated cylinder and pour it into a test tube. With a ruler, measure the height (in cm) and mark the height with a marker.

skip 4. Measure 10.0 mL of water in the graduated cylinder and pour it into a test tube like the one used in the previous step. Again, mark the height with a marker.

In the future, you will often find it convenient to estimate volumes of 5 and 10 mL simply by observing the height of the liquid in the test tube.

E. Density $D = \dfrac{m}{V}$

Estimate and record all volumes to the highest precision, usually 0.1 mL. Make all weighing to the highest precision of the balance. Note that you must supply the units for the measurements and calculations in this section.

1. Density of Water. Weigh a clean, dry 50 mL graduated cylinder and record its mass. *87.084 g* (Graduated cylinders should never be dried over a flame.) Fill the graduated cylinder with distilled water to 50.0 mL. Use a medicine dropper to adjust the meniscus to the 50.0 mL mark. Record the volume. Reweigh and calculate the density of water. *136.047 g*   *Density = .979 g/mL*
50.0 mL

2. Density of a Rubber Stopper. Select a solid rubber stopper which is small enough to fit inside the 50 mL graduated cylinder. Weigh the dry stopper. Fill the 50 mL cylinder with tap water to approximately 25 mL. Read and record the exact volume. Carefully place the rubber stopper into the graduated cylinder so that it is submerged. Read and record the new volume. Calculate the volume and density of the rubber stopper.

DEMO **3. Density of a Solid Object.** Obtain a solid object from your instructor. Record the sample code on the report form. Determine the density of your solid by following the procedure given in Part 2 for the rubber stopper. To avoid the possibility of breakage, incline the graduated cylinder at an angle and slide, rather than drop, the solid into it.

Return the solid object to your instructor.   *Volume of solid object = (Final volume − Initial volume).*

REPORT FOR EXPERIMENT 2

Measurements

A. Temperature

1. Water at room temperature   21.9 °C

2. Boiling point   _____ °C

3. Ice water

   Before stirring   5.5 °C

   After stirring for 1 minute   1.9 °C

4. Ice water with salt added   _____ °C

B. Mass

1. 250 mL beaker   107.860 g

2. 125 mL Erlenmeyer flask   _____ g

3. Weighing paper or weighing boat   2.111 g

4. Mass of weighing paper/boat + sodium chloride   4.103 g

   Mass of sodium chloride (show calculation setup)   1.992 g

   $$4.103 - 2.111 = 1.992$$

C. Length

1. Length of $\longrightarrow$ 5.30 cm

2. Height of 250 mL beaker   8.90 cm

3. Length of test tube   14.69 cm

D. Volume

1. Test tube   30.1 mL

2. 125 mL Erlenmeyer flask   151.1 mL

3. Height of 5.0 mL of water in test tube   _____ cm

4. Height of 10.0 mL of water in test tube   _____ cm

E. Density

1. Density of Water

Mass of empty graduated cylinder   _87.084 g_

Volume of water   _50.0 mL_

Mass of graduated cylinder and water   _136.047 g_

Mass of water (show calculation setup)   _48.963 g_
        136.047 − 87.084 = 48.963

Density of water (show calculation setup)   _.979 g/mL_

$$D = \frac{m}{V} = \frac{48.963}{50.0} = .97926 \ g/mL$$

2. Density of a Rubber Stopper

Mass of rubber stopper   _____

Initial volume of water in cylinder   _____

Final volume of water in cylinder (including stopper)   _____

Volume of rubber stopper (show calculation setup)   _____

Density of rubber stopper (show calculation setup)   _____

3. Density of a Solid Object

Number of solid object   _copper_

Mass of solid object   _56.936 g_

Initial volume of water in graduated cylinder   _24.4 mL_

Final volume in graduated cylinder   _31.0 mL_

Volume of solid object (show calculation setup)   _6.6 mL_
        31.0
      − 24.4
        6.6 mL

Density of solid object (show calculation setup)   _8.6 g/mL_

$$D = \frac{m}{V} = \frac{56.936 \ g}{6.6 \ mL} = 8.6 \ g/mL$$
        (2 sf)

REPORT FOR EXPERIMENT 2 (continued)   NAME TRAN NGUYEN

QUESTIONS AND PROBLEMS

1. The directions state "weigh about 5 grams of sodium chloride". Give minimum and maximum amounts of sodium chloride that would satisfy these instructions.

Minimum = 4.8
Maximum = 5.2

2. Two students each measured the density of a quartz sample three times:

	Student A	Student B	
1.	3.20 g/mL	2.82 g/mL	The density found in the *Handbook*
2.	2.58 g/mL	2.48 g/mL	*of Chemistry and Physics* for quartz
3.	2.10 g/mL	2.59 g/mL	is 2.65 g/mL
mean	2.63 g/mL	2.63 g/mL	

(a) Which student measured density with the greatest precision? Explain your answer.

Student B measured density with the greatest precision, because all data that this student obtained have really similar values. The average of student B measures was 2.63 g/mL, and the average of student A measures was 2.626 g/mL.

(b) Which student measured density with the greatest accuracy? Explain your answer.

Student B measured density with the greatest accuracy because this student's data showed the smallest deviations regarding to the real value (2.65 g/mL). Also, student B's results are closer to each others, not so far like student A.

(c) Are the errors for these students random or systematic? Explain.

The errors for these students are random because if they are systematic, the differences between the measurements would be more precise. Systematic error is any error that has to do w/ equipment but it does not involve any problems w/ the equipment.

Show calculation setups and answers for the following problems.

3. Convert 21°C to degrees Fahrenheit.   69.8°F

$$°F = \frac{9}{5}°C + 32$$
$$= \frac{9}{5}(21) + 32 = 69.8°F$$

4. Convert 101°F to degrees Celsius.   38.3333°C

$$°C = (101°F - 32) \times \frac{5}{9} = 38.3333°C$$

5. An object is 9.6 cm long. What is the length in inches?   3.8 inches

1 inch = 2.54 cm
1 cm = $\frac{1}{2.54}$ inch
9.6 cm = $\frac{1 \times 9.6}{2.54}$ = 3.8 inches

38

6. An empty graduated cylinder weighs 82.450 g. When filled to 50.0 mL with an unknown liquid it weighs 110.810 g. What is the density of the unknown liquid?

$$\begin{array}{r} 110.810 \\ - \ 82.450 \\ \hline 28.360g \end{array}$$

$V = 50.0\,mL$

$D = \dfrac{m}{V} = \dfrac{28.360}{50.0}$

$= 0.5672\,g/mL$

$\underline{0.5672\,g/mL}$

7. It is valuable to know that 1 milliliter (mL) equals 1 cubic centimeter (cm³ or cc). How many cubic centimeters are in an 8.00 oz bottle of cough medicine? (1.00 oz = 29.6 mL)

$29.6\,mL = 29.6\,cm^3$

$8.00\,oz \times 29.6\,cm^3 = 236.8\,cm^3$

$\underline{236.8\,cm^3}$

8. A metal sample weighs 56.8 g. How many ounces does this sample weigh? (1 lb = 16 oz)

$1\,oz = 28.3495\,g$

Mass in ounces $= 56.8\,g \times \dfrac{1\,oz}{28.3495\,g}$

$= 2.00356\,oz$

$\underline{2.00\,oz}$

9. Convert 15 nm into km.

$1\,nm = 10^{-9}\,m$

$15\,nm = 15 \times 10^{-9}\,m$

$1\,m = 10^{-3}\,km$

$\underline{1.5 \times 10^{-11}\,km}$

Therefore, $15 \times 10^{-9}\,m = 15 \times 10^{-9} \times 10^{-3}\,km = 1.5 \times 10^{-11}\,km$

Hence, $15\,nm = 1.5 \times 10^{-11}\,km$

Experiment 3   Separation of a mixture

Mixtures are not unique to chemistry; we use and consume them on a daily basis. The beverages we drink each morning, the fuel we use in our automobiles, and the ground we walk on are mixtures. Very few materials we encounter are pure. Any material made up of two or more substances that are not chemically combined is a mixture. The isolation of pure components of a mixture requires the separation of one component from another. There are several techniques to do this that take advantage of the differences in physical properties of the components. Techniques that can be used to separate mixtures are:

1. **Sublimation**: Heating the solid until it passes directly from the solid phase to the gaseous phase. Solids which sublime are iodine, caffeine, and para-dichlorobenzene (mothballs).

2. **Extraction**: Using a solvent to selectively dissolve one component from the solid mixture. A soluble solid can be separated from an insoluble solid.

3. **Decantation**: Separating a liquid from an insoluble solid sediment by carefully pouring the liquid from the solid without disturbing the solid.

4. **Filtration**: Separating a solid from a liquid through the use of a porous material such as a filter. Paper, charcoal, or sand can serve as a filter.

5. **Evaporation**: Heating a mixture in order to drive off, in the form of a vapor, a volatile liquid, so as to make the remaining component dry. The mixture that will be separated in this experiment contains two components: common table salt (NaCl), and sea sand (SiO_2). This will be accomplished by − dissolving the table salt with water to extract the salt, and − evaporating the water to recover dry NaCl and sand.

Procedure

Step One:

Select one of the unknowns.and record the number of the unknown. Using approximately 5 grams and a mortar and pestal, grind the sample of mixture to a fine powder. Transfer approximately 2 g of the unknown mixture onto a weighing paper that has already been zeroed on the balance. Weigh the sample . record the value to the third decimal place in your data table (1) Transfer the solid to a 150mL beaker Add 25 mL of distilled water to the solid in the beaker. Heat and stir for 5 minutes. Weigh a clean evaporating dish record the value in your data table (2)

Step Two

Fold a piece of filter paper as demonstrated by your instructor and place the filter paper in a glass funnel. Place the funnel in a ring stand with a 150-mL beaker underneath the funnel. Your instructor will demonstrate this set up on the front bench. Pour the mixture through the filter, first decanting most of the liquid then transferring the wet solid into the funnel with a clean rubber policeman. Rinse the first beaker with 5-10 mL of water, pour this over the residue in the funnel. Transfer the filtrate to the weighed evaporating dish and place it on a wire gauze on a ring stand. Heat the evaporating dish with a Bunsen burner. As the water evaporates, solid NaCl will appear. Reduce the flame to avoid "spattering. When the liquid is gone, cool the evaporating dish to room temperature. Weight the dish, and solid residue (3). Calculate the weight of the NaCl. [(3) – (2)] (4)

Step three:

Weigh a second clean, evaporating dish (5)). Transfer the sand from the filter paper to the evaporation dish . Heat the sand to dryness CAREFULLY to avoid spattering. When dry, the sand will be freely flowing. Allow the sand to cool to room temperature. Weigh the evaporating dish and the sand (6). Calculate the weight of the sand [(6) – (5)] (7).

To calculate the percentage of each component in the mixture:

$$\% \text{ component} = \frac{\text{grams of component} \times 100}{\text{grams of sample}}$$

$$\% \, NaCl = \frac{\text{grams salt}}{\text{grams of total}} \times 100$$

EXPERIMENT 7

Water in Hydrates

MATERIALS AND EQUIPMENT

Solids: finely ground copper(II) sulfate pentahydrate ($CuSO_4 \cdot 5H_2O$), and unknown hydrate. Cobalt chloride test paper, clay triangle, crucible and cover, 25 × 200 mm ignition test tube, watch glass.

DISCUSSION

Many salts form compounds in which a definite number of moles of water are combined with each mole of the anhydrous salt. Such compounds are called **hydrates.** The water which is chemically combined in a hydrate is referred to as **water of crystallization** or **water of hydration.** The following are representative examples:

$$CaSO_4 \cdot 2H_2O, \quad CoCl_2 \cdot 6H_2O, \quad MgSO_4 \cdot 7H_2O, \quad Na_2CO_3 \cdot 10H_2O$$

In a hydrate the water molecules are distinct parts of the compound but are joined to it by bonds that are weaker than either those forming the anhydrous salt or those forming the water molecules. In the formula of a hydrate a dot is commonly used to separate the formula of the anhydrous salt from the number of molecules of water of crystallization. For example, the formula of calcium sulfate dihydrate is written $CaSO_4 \cdot 2H_2O$ rather than $CaSO_6H_4$.

Hydrated salts can usually be converted to the anhydrous form by careful heating:

$$\text{Hydrated Salt} \xrightarrow{\Delta} \text{Anhydrous salt} + \text{water}$$

Hydrated salts can be studied qualitatively and quantitatively. In the **qualitative** part of this experiment we will observe some of properties of the liquid (water) driven off by heating the sample. In the **quantitative** part of the experiment we will determine **how much** water was in the hydrate by measuring the amount of water driven off by heating.

To make certain that all of the water in the original sample has been driven off, chemists use a technique known as **heating to constant weight.** Since time expended for this is limited, constant weight is essentially achieved when the sample is heated and weighed in successive heatings until the weight differs by no more than 0.05 g. Thus, if the second weighing is no more than 0.05 g less than the first heating, a third heating is not necessary because the sample has been heated to constant weight (almost). This is a very good reason to follow directions meticulously when heating. If the sample is not heated long enough or at the correct temperature, all of the water may not be driven off completely in the first heating.

Hence it is possible to determine the percentage of water in a hydrated salt by determining the amount of mass lost (water driven off) when a known mass of the hydrate is heated to constant weight.

$$\text{Percentage water} = \left(\frac{\text{Mass lost}}{\text{Mass of sample}} \right)(100)$$

It is possible to condense the vapor driven off the hydrate and demonstrate that it is water by testing it with anhydrous cobalt(II) chloride ($CoCl_2$). Anhydrous cobalt(II) chloride is blue but reacts with water to form the red hexahydrate, $CoCl_2 \cdot 6H_2O$.

PROCEDURE

Wear protective glasses.

A. Qualitative Determination of Water

1. Fold a 2.5 × 20 cm strip of paper lengthwise to form a V-shaped trough or chute. Load about 4 g of finely ground copper(II) sulfate pentahydrate in this trough, spreading it evenly along the length of the trough.

2. Clamp a **dry** 25 × 200 mm ignition test tube so that its mouth is 15–20 degrees **above the horizontal** (Figure 7.1a). Insert the loaded trough into the tube. Rotate the tube to a nearly vertical position (Figure 7.1b) to deposit the copper(II) sulfate in the bottom of the tube. Tap the paper chute gently if necessary, but make sure that no copper sulfate is spilled and adhering to the sides of the upper part of the tube.

3. Remove the chute and turn the tube until it slants mouth downward at an angle of 15–20 degrees **below the horizontal** (Figure 7.1c). Make sure that all of the copper(II) sulfate remains at the bottom of the tube. To obtain a sample of the liquid that will condense in the cooler part of the tube, place a clean, dry test tube, held in an upright position in either a rack or an Erlenmeyer flask, just below the mouth of the tube containing the hydrate.

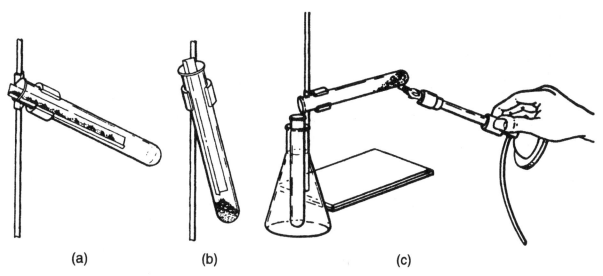

(a)　　　　　　　(b)　　　　　　　(c)

Figure 7.1　Setup for dehydration of a hydrate

4. Heat the hydrate gently at first to avoid excessive spattering. Gradually increase the rate of heating, noting any changes that occur and collecting some of the liquid that condenses in the cooler part of the tube. Continue heating until the blue color of the hydrate has disappeared, but do not heat until the residue in the tube has turned black. Finally warm the tube over its entire length—without directly applying the flame to the clamp—for a minute

or two to drive off most of the liquid that has condensed on the inner wall of the tube. Allow the tube and contents to cool.

> **NOTE:** At excessively high temperatures (above 600°C) copper(II) sulfate decomposes; sulfur trioxide is driven off and the black copper(II) oxide remains as a residue.

Observe and record the appearance and odor of the liquid that has been collected.

5. While the tube is cooling, dry a piece of cobalt chloride test paper by holding it with tongs about 20 to 25 cm above a burner flame; that is, close enough to heat but not close enough to char or ignite the paper. When properly dried, the test paper should be blue. Using a clean stirring rod, place a drop of the liquid collected from the hydrate on the dried cobalt chloride test paper. For comparison place a drop of distilled water on the cobalt chloride paper. Record your observations.

6. Empty the anhydrous salt residue in the tube onto a watch glass and divide it into two portions. Add 3 or 4 drops of the liquid collected from the hydrate to one portion and 3 or 4 drops of distilled water to the other. Compare and record the results of these tests.

 Dispose of solid residues in the waste heavy metal container provided.

B. Quantitative Determination of Water in a Hydrate

> **NOTES:**
>
> 1. **Weigh crucible and contents to the highest precision with the balance available to you.**
>
> 2. Since there is some inaccuracy in any balance, use the same balance for successive weighings of the same sample. When subtractions are made to give mass of sample and mass lost, the inaccuracy due to the balance should cancel out.
>
> 3. Handle crucibles and covers with tongs only, after initial heating.
>
> 4. Be sure crucibles are at or near room temperature when weighed.
>
> 5. **Record all data directly on the report form as soon as you obtain them.**

sample: 2.651 g

1. Obtain a sample of an unknown hydrate, as directed by your instructor. Be sure to record the identifying number.

2. Weigh a clean, dry crucible and cover to the highest precision of the balance. (1) 20.534 g

3. Place between 2 and 3 g of the unknown into the weighed crucible. Cover and weigh the crucible and contents. (2) 23.185 g

Experiment 8   What Ions are in Your Water?

Introduction

Water naturally contains many ions; some are beneficial to and even necessary for human health, and some are quite hazardous, even in very low concentrations. To confirm that certain ions are present in a sample, you can add another ion that will react in a predictable way with the ion in question. Typically, a **color change** occurs or an insoluble material, called a **_precipitate_**, is produced.

The tests you will perform are confirming tests. If the test is positive you can be sure the ion in question is present. However, a negative test (no color change or no precipitate formed) does not necessarily mean the ion in question is not present. The ion may simply be present in such a small amount that human eyes cannot see the color change or precipitate. (Reagents = 0.1 M concentrations of the ions listed below)

Objective: To test water samples for the presence of various "pollutants":
Calcium ion, Ca^{2+} Iron (III), Fe^{3+} Chloride, Cl^{1-} Sulfate, SO_4^{2-}

By testing with these ions:
**Carbonate, CO_3^{2-} Thiocyanide, SCN^{1-} Silver ion, Ag^{1+}
Barium ion, Ba^{2+}**

Safety: At low concentrations such as these, these chemicals are not dangerous, but should not be ingested, and skin contact should be avoided as much as possible. Silver ion (Ag^{1+}) may cause a brown stain if it contacts your skin or clothes.

To avoid contamination, once you have taken chemicals from a source container, do not put them back into the container!

Procedure:

Part I: Determine which chemicals test for the presence of each "pollutant".

1. Set aside 4 test tubes and fill each with one mL of Ca^{2+} ion, Label: 1,2,3,4.

2. Add 1 mL of CO_3^{2-} ion solution to test tube #1
   Add 1 mL of SCN^{1-} ion solution to test tube #2
   Add 1 mL of Ag^{1+} ion solution to test tube #3
   Add 1 mL of Ba^{2+} ion solution to test tube #4

3. Record your observations in **Table I** that follows. Record observations of any changes in color or consistency; use "NR" if No Reaction occurs.

4. Repeat the above procedure for Fe^{3+}, Cl^{1-}, and SO_4^{2-}

Part II. Testing of water samples

1. Test a sample of distilled water (control) for the presence of each "pollutant".
   Use 1 mL samples and perform only the test that gave a reaction in Part I
   If you actually observe no reaction write NR in the spaces for the distilled water. In Table II. (note this is a control and you should not observe any reactions, however a control is necessary to insure that the procedures were properly performed.)

2. Test a sample of tap water for the presence of each "pollutant".
   Use 1 mL samples and perform the tests that gave a reaction in Part I
   Record your observations in Table II

3. Repeat the above for river water and record your observations in Table II

4. Record the ions (Ca^{2+}, Fe^{3+}, Cl^{1-}, and/or SO_4^{2-}) found present in the tap water and the river water in the **last row of Table II**

Part III. Write balanced equations showing what happened in each test tube where a reaction occurred. Note: Why should there be no reactions between two cations (e.g. Ag^+ and Ca^{2+}) or two anions (e.g. SCN^- and Cl^-)?

Example: $Ca^{+2} + CO_3^{-2} \rightarrow CaCO_3$

REPORT SHEET **EXPERIMENT 8**

Name Tran Nguyen

Table I

ppt (precipitate).

	Ca^{2+}	Fe^{3+}	Cl^{1-}	SO_4^{2-}	← **Polutants**
CO_3^{2-}	↓white	↓brown/orange	NR	NR	
SCN^{1-}	clear	dark red	NR	NR	
Ag^{1+}	NR	NR	cloudy white	clear	
Ba^{2+}	NR	NR	clear	cloudy white	

^
Test Ions

Result:
1. To test for Calcium Ion I will use CO_3^{2-}
2. To tset for Iron Ion I will use SCN^{1-}
3. To test for Chloride Ion I will use Ag^{+}
4. To test for Sulfate Ion I will use Ba^{2+}

Table II

Test Solutions →	**Control (Distilled H_2O)**	**Test (Tap H_2O)**	**Test (River Water)** Nile
CO_3^{2-}	NR	NR	orange (ppt)
SCN^{1-}	NR	NR	dark red
Ag^{1+}	NR	cloudy white	NR
Ba^{2+}	NR	NR	white
Ions Present →	None	Cl^{1-}	Fe^{3+}, SO_4^{2-}

Part III **Complete the following by supplying the correct molecular formula:**

$Ca^{2+} + CO_3^{2-} = CaCO_3$

$Ca^{2+} + 2SCN^{1-} = Ca(SCN)_2$

$2Fe^{3+} + 3CO_3^{2-} = Fe_2(CO_3)_3$

$Fe^{3+} + 3SCN^{1-} = Fe(SCN)_3$

$Ag^{1+} + Cl^{1-} = AgCl$

$2Ag^{1+} + SO_4^{2-} = Ag_2SO_4$

$Ba^{2+} + 2Cl^{1-} = BaCl_2$

$Ba^{2+} + SO_4^{2-} = BaSO_4$

EXPERIMENT 8

Name Tran Nguyen

Post-lab Questions:

1. Are these tests qualitative or quantitative? Explain.

2. Is it possible for an ion to be present but not detected in the test?

3. What is a *control*? Why/how was it used in this test?

4. Why was distilled water chosen as the *control*?

EXPERIMENT 9

Properties of Solutions

MATERIALS AND EQUIPMENT

Solids: ammonium chloride (NH_4Cl), barium chloride ($BaCl_2$), barium sulfate ($BaSO_4$), fine and coarse crystals of sodium chloride (NaCl), and sodium sulfate (Na_2SO_4). **Liquids:** decane ($C_{10}H_{22}$), isopropyl alcohol (C_3H_7OH), and kerosene. **Solutions:** saturated iodine-water (I_2), and saturated potassium chloride (KCl).

DISCUSSION

Solute, Solvent, and Solution

The term **solution** is used in chemistry to describe a homogeneous mixture in which at least one substance (the **solute**) is dissolved in another substance (the **solvent**). The solvent is the substance present in greater quantity and the name of the solution is taken from the name of the solute. Thus, when sodium chloride is dissolved in water, sodium chloride is the solute, water is the solvent, and the solution is called a sodium chloride solution.

In this experiment we will be working with two common types of solutions: those in which a solid solute is dissolved in a liquid solvent (water), and a few in which a liquid solute is dissolved in a liquid solvent.

Like other mixtures, a solution has variable composition, since more or less solute can be dissolved in a given quantity of a solvent. The amount of solute that remains uniformly dispersed throughout the solution after mixing is referred to as the **solution concentration** and can be expressed in many different ways. The maximum concentration that a solution can have varies depending on many factors, including the temperature, the kind of particles in the solute, and interactions between the solute particles and the solvent. In general, water, which is polar, is a better solvent for inorganic than for organic substances. On the other hand, nonpolar solvents such as benzene, decane, and ether are good solvents for many organic substances that are practically insoluble in water.

Dissolved solute particles can be either molecules or ions and their size is of the order of 10^{-8} to 10^{-7} cm (1-10 Å). Many substances will react chemically with each other only when they are dissociated into ions in solution. For example, when the two solids sodium chloride (NaCl) and silver nitrate ($AgNO_3$) are mixed, no detectable reaction is observed. However, when aqueous solutions of these salts are mixed, their component ions react immediately to form a white precipitate (AgCl).

The rate at which a solute and solvent will form a solution depends on several factors, all of which are related to the amount of contact between the solute particles and the solvent. A solid can dissolve only at the surface that is in contact with the solvent. Any change which increases that contact will increase the rate of solution and vice versa. Thus, the rate of dissolving a solid solute depends on:

1. The particle size of the solute
2. Agitation or stirring of the solution
3. The temperature of the solution
4. The concentration of the solute in solution

Solubility, Miscibility, and Concentration

The term **solubility** refers to the maximum amount of solute that will dissolve in a specified amount of solvent under stated conditions. At a specific temperature, there is a limit to the amount of solute that will dissolve in a given amount of solvent.

Solubility can be expressed in a relative, qualitative way. For example a solute may be very soluble, moderately soluble, slightly soluble, or insoluble in a given solvent at a given temperature. Table 8.1 shows how temperature effects the amount of four different salts that dissolve in 100 g of water.

Table 9.1
Temperature Effect on Solubility of Four Salts in Water, g solute/100 g water

	0°C	10°C	20°C	30°C	40°C	50°C	60°C	70°C	80°C	90°C	100°C
KCl	27.6	31.0	34.0	37.0	40.0	42.6	45.5	48.3	51.1	54.0	55.6
NaCl	35.7	35.8	36.0	36.3	36.6	37.0	37.3	37.8	38.4	39.0	39.8
KBr	53.5	59.5	65.2	70.6	75.5	80.2	85.5	90.0	95.0	99.2	104.0
BaCl$_2$	31.6	33.3	35.7	38.2	40.7	43.6	46.6	49.4	52.6	55.7	58.8

The term **miscibility** describes the solubility of two liquids in each other. When both the solute and solvent are liquids, their solubility in each other is described as miscible (soluble) or immiscible (insoluble). For example, ethyl alcohol and water are miscible; oil and water are immiscible.

The **concentration** of a solution expresses how much solute is dissolved in solution and can be expressed several ways:

1. **Dilute vs. Concentrated:** a dilute solution contains a relatively small amount of solute in a given volume of solution; a concentrated solution contains a relatively large amount of solute per unit volume of solution.

2. **Saturated vs. Unsaturated vs. Supersaturated:**

a. A **saturated** solution contains as much dissolved solute as possible at a given temperature and pressure. The dissolved solute is in equilibrium with undissolved solute. A saturated solution can be dilute or concentrated. The solutions described in Table 8.1 are saturated at each temperature.

Solute (solid) $\rightleftharpoons$ Solute (dissolved)

b. **Unsaturated** solutions contain less solute per unit volume than the corresponding saturated solution. Thus, more solute will dissolve in an unsaturated solution (until saturation is reached).

c. **Supersaturated** solutions contain more dissolved solute than is normally present in the corresponding saturated solution. However, a supersaturated solution is in a very unstable state and will form a saturated solution if disturbed. For example, when a small crystal of the dissolved salt is dropped into a supersaturated solution, crystallization begins at once and salt precipitates until a saturated solution is formed.

3. **Mass-percent Solution** is a quantitative expression of concentration expressed as the percent by mass of the solute in a solution. For example, a 10% sodium hydroxide solution contains 10 g of NaOH in 100 g of solution (10 g NaOH + 90 g H_2O); 2 g NaOH in 20 g of solution (2 g NaOH + 18 g H_2O). The formula for calculating mass percent is:

$$\text{Mass percent} = \left(\frac{\text{g solute}}{\text{g solute} + \text{g solvent}}\right)(100)$$

4. **Mass per 100 g solvent** is another quantitative expression of concentration (and the one used in Table 8.1). It is not the same as the Mass percent concentration above because the units are g solute/100 g solvent. Thus, for the 10% NaOH solution described in No. 3, the g NaOH/100 g H_2O would be calculated as follows:

$$\left(\frac{10\,\text{g NaOH}}{90\,\text{g }H_2O}\right)(100) = \frac{11\,\text{g NaOH}}{100\,\text{g }H_2O}$$

5. **Molarity** is the most common quantitative expression of concentration. Molarity is the number of moles (molar mass) of solute per liter of solution. Thus a solution containing 1 mole of NaOH (40.00 g) per liter is 1 molar (abbreviated 1 M). The concentration of a solution containing 0.5 mole in 500 mL (0.5 L) is also 1 M. The formula for calculating molarity is:

$$\text{Molarity} = \frac{\text{moles of solute}}{\text{liter of solution}} = \frac{\text{moles}}{\text{liter}}$$

PROCEDURE

Wear protective glasses.

A. Concentration of a Saturated Solution

> Use the same balance for all weighings.
> Make all weighings to the highest precision of the balance.

1. Prepare a water bath with a 400 mL beaker half full of tap water and heat to boiling. (See Figure 1.6.)

2. Weigh an empty evaporating dish. Obtain 6 mL of saturated potassium chloride solution and pour it into the dish. Weigh the dish with the solution in it and record these masses on the report form.

3. Place the evaporating dish on the beaker of boiling water and continue to boil until the potassium chloride solution has evaporated almost to dryness (about 25 to 30 minutes), **adding more water to the beaker as needed.**

While the evaporation is proceeding, continue with other parts of the experiment.

4. Remove the evaporating dish and beaker from the wire gauze and dry the bottom of the dish with a towel. Put the dish on the wire gauze and heat gently for 1-2 minutes to evaporate the last traces of water. Do not heat too strongly because at high temperatures there is danger of sample loss by spattering.

5. Allow the dish with dry potassium chloride to cool on the Ceramfab pad for 5 to 10 minutes and weigh. To be sure that all the water has evaporated from the potassium chloride, put the dish back on the wire gauze and heat gently again for 1-2 minutes.

6. Allow the dish to cool again on the Ceramfab pad for 5 to 10 minutes and reweigh. The second weighing should be no more than 0.05 g less than the first weighing. Otherwise a third heating and weighng should be done.

 7. Add water to the residue in the dish to redissolve the potassium chloride. Pour the solution into the sink and flush generously with water.

B. Relative Solubility of a Solute in Two Solvents

1. Add about 2 mL of decane and 5 mL of water to a test tube, stopper it, and shake gently for about 5 seconds. Allow the liquid layers to separate and note which liquid has the greatest density.

2. Now, add 5 mL of saturated iodine-water to the test tube, note the color of each layer, insert the stopper, and shake gently for about 20 seconds. Allow the liquids to separate and again note the color of each layer.

 3. Dispose of the mixture in this test tube in the bottle labeled **Decane Waste.**

C. Miscibility of Liquids

1. Take three dry test tubes and add liquids to each as follows:

a. 1 mL kerosene and 1 mL isopropyl alcohol

b. 1 mL kerosene and 1 mL water

c. 1 mL water and 1 mL isopropyl alcohol

2. Stopper each tube and mix by shaking for about 5 seconds. Note which pairs are miscible. Dispose of the kerosene mixtures (a and b) in the bottle labeled **Kerosene Waste.** Dispose the contents in test tube (c) in the sink.

D. Effect of Particle Size on Rate of Dissolving

1. Fill a dry test tube to a depth of about 0.5 cm with fine crystals of sodium chloride. Fill another dry tube to the same depth with coarse sodium chloride crystals. Add 10 mL of tap water to each tube and stopper. Shake both tubes at the same time, noting the number of seconds required to dissolve the salt in each tube. (Don't shake the tubes for more than two minutes.)

 2. Dispose of these solutions in the sink.

E. Effect of Temperature on Rate of Dissolving

1. Weigh two 0.5 g samples of fine sodium chloride crystals.

2. Take a 100 mL and a 150 mL beaker and add 50 mL tap water to each. Heat the water in the 150 mL beaker to boiling and allow it to cool for about 1 minute.

3. Add the 0.5 g samples of salt to each beaker and observe the time necessary for the crystals to dissolve in the hot water (do not stir).

4. As soon as the crystals are dissolved in the hot water, take the beaker containing the hot solution in your hand, slowly tilt it back and forth, and observe the layer of denser salt solution on the bottom. Repeat with the cold-water solution.

 5. Dispose of these solutions in the sink.

F. Solubility versus Temperature; Saturated and Unsaturated Solutions

1. Label four weighing boats or papers as follows and weigh the stated amounts onto each one.

   a. 1.0 g NaCl   b. 1.4 g NaCl   c. 1.0 g NH_4Cl d. 1.4 g NH_4Cl

2. Record observations in the table provided on the report form as you proceed through 3-6.

3. Add the 1.0 g samples of NaCl and NH_4Cl to separate tubes labeled A and B as shown. Add 5 mL of distilled water to each, stopper and shake until each salt is dissolved.

4. Now add 1.4 g NaCl to test tube A. Add 1.4 g NH_4Cl to test tube B. Stopper and shake for about 3 minutes. Note whether all of the crystals have dissolved.

5. Place both tubes (unstoppered) into a beaker of boiling water, shake occasionally, and note the results after about 5 minutes.

6. Remove the tubes and cool in running tap water for about 1 minute. Let stand for a few minutes and record what you observe.

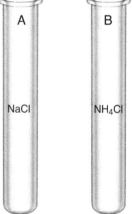

 7. Dispose of these solutions in the sink. Flush generously with water.

G. Ionic Reactions in Solution

1. Into four labeled test tubes, place pea-sized quantities of the following salts, one salt in each tube: (a) barium chloride, (b) sodium sulfate, (c) sodium chloride, (d) barium sulfate.

2. Add 5 mL of water to each tube, stopper, and shake to dissolve. One of the four salts does not dissolve.

3. Mix the barium chloride and sodium sulfate solutions together. Note the results. (Sodium chloride and barium sulfate are the products of this reaction.)

 Dispose of all tubes containing barium in the waste bottle provided. The remaining tubes can be rinsed in the sink.

REPORT FOR EXPERIMENT 9

Properties of Solutions

A.   Concentration of Saturated Solution

1. Mass of empty evaporating dish   _____

2. Mass of dish + saturated potassium chloride solution   _____

3. Mass of dish + dry potassium chloride, 1st heating   _____

4. Mass of dish + dry potassium chloride, 2nd heating   _____

5. Mass of saturated potassium chloride solution   _____
    Show Calculation Setup

6. Mass of potassium chloride in the saturated solution   _____
    Show Calculation Setup

7. Mass of water in the saturated potassium chloride solution   _____
    Show Calculation Setup

8. Mass percent of potassium chloride in the saturated solution   _____
    Show Calculation Setup

9. Grams of potassium chloride per 100 g of water (experimental)   _____
    in the original solution.
    Show Calculation Setup

10. Grams of potassium chloride per 100 g of water (theoretical)   _____
    (From Table 8.1) at 20°C.

B. Relative Solubility of a Solute in Two Solvents

1. (a) Which liquid is denser, decane or water?   _____

    (b) What experimental evidence supports your answer?

2. Color of iodine in water: _____

    Color of iodine in decane: _____

3. (a) In which of the two solvents used is iodine more soluble?   _____

    (b) Cite experimental evidence for your answer.

C. Miscibility of Liquids

1. Which liquid pairs tested are miscible?

2. How do you classify the liquid pair decane—H_2O, miscible or immiscible?

                        _____

D. Rate of Dissolving Versus Particle Size

1. Time required for fine salt crystals to dissolve   _____

2. Time required for coarse salt crystals to dissolve   _____

3. Since the amount of salt, the volume of water, and the temperature of the systems were identical in both test tubes, how do you explain the difference in time for dissolving the fine vs. the coarse salt crystals?

E. Rate of Dissolving Versus Temperature

1. Under which condition, hot or cold, did the salt dissolve faster?   _____

2. Since the amount of salt, the volume of water, and the texture of the salt crystals were identical in both best tubes, how do you explain the difference in time for dissolving at the hot vs. cold temperatures?

F. Solubility vs. Temperature; Saturated and Unsaturated Solutions

Data Table: Circle the choices which best describe your observations.

	NaCl	**NH₄Cl**
1.0 g + 5 mL water	dissolved completely? yes/no saturated or unsaturated?	dissolved completely? yes/no saturated or unsaturated?
1.0 g + 5 mL water + 1.4 g	dissolved completely? yes/no saturated or unsaturated?	dissolved completely? yes/no saturated or unsaturated?
2.4 g + 5 mL water + heat	dissolved completely? yes/no saturated or unsaturated?	dissolved completely? yes/no saturated or unsaturated?
2.4 g + 5 mL water after cooling	dissolved completely? yes/no saturated or unsaturated?	dissolved completely? yes/no saturated or unsaturated?

G. Ionic Reactions in Solution

1. Write the word and formula equations representing the chemical reaction that occurred between the barium chloride solution, $BaCl_2(aq)$, and the sodium sulfate solution, $Na_2SO_4(aq)$.

   Word Equation:

   Formula Equation:

2. (a) Which of the products is the white precipitate?   _____

   (b) What experimental evidence leads you to this conclusion?

SUPPLEMENTARY QUESTIONS AND PROBLEMS

1. Use the solubility data in Table 9.1 to answer the following:
   Show Calculations

   (a) What is the percentage by mass of NaCl in a saturated solution of sodium chloride at 50°C?

_____

(b) Calculate the solubility of potassium bromide at 23°C. Hint: Assume that the solubility increases by an equal amount for each degree between 20°C and 30°C.

_____

(c) A saturated solution of barium chloride at 30°C contains 150 g water. How much additional barium chloride can be dissolved by heating this solution to 60°C?

_____

2. A solution of KCl is saturated at 50°C.
   Use Table 9.1

   (a) How many grams of solute are dissolved in 100 g of water?   _____

   (b) What is the total mass of the solution?   _____

   (c) What is the mass percent of this solution at 50°C?   _____

   (d) If the solution is heated to 100°C, how much more KCl can be dissolved in the solution without adding more water?

   _____

   (e) If the solution is saturated at 100°C and then cooled to 30°C, how many grams of solute will precipitate out?

   _____

Experiment 10 Determining an Empirical Formula

DISCUSSION
In a sample of a compound, regardless of the size of the sample, the number of moles of one element in the sample divided by the number of moles of another element in the sample will form a small whole-number ratio. These small whole-number ratios can be used to determine the subscripts in the empirical formula of the compound. For example, suppose that in a 48-gram sample of a compound, there are 36 g of carbon (3.0 moles of carbon) and 12 g of hydrogen (12 moles of hydrogen). These numbers form the small whole-number ratio of I to 4:

$$\frac{3.0 \text{ moles of carbon}}{12 \text{ moles hydrogen}} = \frac{1}{4}$$

The 1-to-4 ratio means that for every 1 atom of carbon in the compound, there are 4 atoms of hydrogen. The empirical formula of the compound is CH_4. (The compound's name is methane.)

In this experiment, the number of moles of each of two elements in a binary compound will be experimentally determined. From this information, the empirical formula of the compound will be determined. This experiment will help you understand better the concepts of molar masses and empirical formulas.

PURPOSE
Using mass relationships show that copper and chlorine combine in a definite whole-number ratio by mass.

EQUIPMENT Buchner Funnel, 20 gauge Al wire, scissors , filter paper, 50 mL beaker

MATERIALS Anhydrous Copper (II) chloride, 95% ethanol

PROCEDURE:
1) Weigh out apprx.0.50 grams of the unknown anhydrous copper chloride on weighing paper (make all weighings to the third decimal place). Transfer the crystals to a 50 mL beaker and dissolve in 20 mL of distilled water.
2) When the crystals are dissolved, coil a 15-20 cm length of 20 gauge Al wire. Place the wire in the solution so that it is completely immersed You should begin to observe the evolution of hydrogen gas and the formation of copper on the wire. Stir the solution with a glass stirring rod to help remove the copper as it forms.
3) When the reaction is complete, about 15-20 minutes the solution should be colorless and most of the copper should be on the bottom of the beaker or on the wire. Use your glass stirring rod to dislodge all the remaining copper particles from the wire
4) Set up a Buchner funnel as demonstrated by your instructor. Weigh a piece of filter paper that will fit the funnel. Wet the paper and try the suction. With the suction on decant the copper particles into the funnel. Make sure that all of the copper is deposited on the filter paper. Rinse the beaker with distilled water if necessary.
5) Add 10 mL of 95% ethanol to the copper in the funnel with the suction on. Remove the filter paper and copper and dry under a heating lamp for 5 minutes. After it cools weigh it.
6) Calculate the formula of the copper chloride. If time permits run a second trial.

Experiment 10 Report Sheet

Name_____ Unknown Number_____

	Trial 1	**Trial 2**
a) Mass of unknown CuxCly	_____ g.	_____ g
b) Mass of filter paper	_____ g	_____ g
c) Mass of filter paper + Copper	_____ g	_____ g
d) Mass of Copper	_____ g	_____ g
e) Moles of Copper in Compound	_____ mol	_____ mol
f) Mass of Chlorine in Compound	_____ g	_____ g
g) Moles of Chlorine in Compound	_____ mol	_____ mol
h) Ratio of moles of Cl to Moles of Cu	_____	_____
i) Formula of the copper chloride	_____	_____

CALCULATIONS

QUESTIONS

1. What is the ratio of the mass in grams of copper used to the mass in grams of chlorine that are in the compound?

2. The molecular formula of hydrogen bromide is H_2Br_2. What is the empirical formula?

3. A sample of sulfur having a mass of 2.56 g combines with oxygen to form a compound with a mass of 6.40 g. What is the empirical formula of the compound?

ADDITIONAL PROBLEMS (Optional, see your instructor)

1. A sample of $CaSO_4$ weighs 86.0 g

a) Calculate the Molar Mass of the compound ?

b) Calculate the number of moles in the sample ?

2. Calculate the empirical formula of the following compound ?
49.3% C, 9.60% H, 22.0% O, & 19.1% N,

2. Isoprene can be polymerized to form natural rubber. It contains 88.2% Carbon and 11.8% Hydrogen. It has a Molar Mass of 136 g/mol.

a) Calculate the Empirical Formula ?

b) Molecular Formula ?

EXPERIMENT 11

Double Displacement Reactions

MATERIALS AND EQUIPMENT

Solid: sodium sulfite (Na_2SO_3). **Solutions:** dilute (6 M) ammonium hydroxide (NH_4OH), 0.1 M ammonium chloride (NH_4Cl), 0.1 M barium chloride ($BaCl_2$), 0.1 M calcium chloride ($CaCl_2$), 0.1 M copper(II) sulfate ($CuSO_4$), dilute (6 M) hydrochloric acid (HCl), concentrated (12 M) hydrochloric acid (HCl), 0.1 M iron(III) chloride ($FeCl_3$), dilute (6 M) nitric acid (HNO_3), 0.1 M potassium nitrate (KNO_3), 0.1 M silver nitrate ($AgNO_3$), 0.1 M sodium carbonate (Na_2CO_3), 0.1 M sodium chloride (NaCl), 10 percent sodium hydroxide (NaOH), dilute (3 M) sulfuric acid (H_2SO_4), and 0.1 M zinc nitrate [$Zn(NO_3)_2$]. Medicine dropper.

DISCUSSION

Double displacement reactions are among the most common of the simple chemical reactions and are comparatively easy to study.

In each part of this experiment two aqueous solutions, each containing positive and negative ions, will be mixed in a test tube. Consider the hypothetical reaction.

$$AB + CD \longrightarrow AD + CB$$

where AB(aq) exists as A^+ and B^- ions in solution and CD(aq) exists as C^+ and D^- ions in solution. As the ions come in contact with each other, there are six possible combinations that might conceivably cause chemical reaction. Two of these combinations are the meeting of ions of like charge; that is, $A^+ + C^+$ and $B^- + D^-$. But since like charges repel, no reaction will occur. Two other possible combinations are those of the original two compounds; that is, $A^+ + B^-$ and $C^+ + D^-$. Since we originally had a solution containing each of these pairs of ions, they can mutually exist in the same solution; therefore they do not recombine. Thus the two possibilities for chemical reaction are the combination of each of the positive ions with the negative ion of the other compound; that is, $A^+ + D^-$ and $C^+ + B^-$. Let us look at some examples.

Example 1. When solutions of sodium chloride and potassium nitrate are mixed, the equation for the double displacement reaction (hypothetical) is

$$NaCl(aq) + KNO_3(aq) \longrightarrow KCl(aq) + NaNO_3(aq)$$

We get the hypothetical products by simply combining each positive ion with the other negative ion. But has there been a reaction? When we do the experiment, we see no evidence of reaction. There is no precipitate formed, no gas evolved, and no obvious temperature change. Thus we must conclude that no reaction occurred. Both hypothetical products are soluble salts, so the ions are still present in solution. We can say that we simply have a solution of four kinds of ions, Na^+, Cl^-, K^+, and NO_3^-.

The situation is best expressed by changing the equation to

$$NaCl(aq) + KNO_3(aq) \longrightarrow No\ reaction$$

Example 2. When solutions of sodium chloride and silver nitrate are mixed, the equation for the double displacement reaction (hypothetical) is

$$NaCl + AgNO_3 \longrightarrow NaNO_3 + AgCl$$

A white precipitate is produced when these solutions are mixed. This precipitate is definite evidence of a chemical reaction. One of the two products, sodium nitrate ($NaNO_3$) or silver chloride ($AgCl$), is insoluble. Although the precipitate can be identified by further chemical testing, we can instead look at the **Solubility Table in Appendix 5** to find that sodium nitrate is soluble but silver chloride is insoluble. We may then conclude that the precipitate is silver chloride and indicate this in the equation with an (s). Thus

$$NaCl(aq) + AgNO_3(aq) \longrightarrow NaNO_3(aq) + AgCl(s)$$

Example 3. When solutions of sodium carbonate and hydrochloric acid are mixed, the equation for the double displacement reaction (hypothetical) is

$$Na_2CO_3(aq) + 2\,HCl(aq) \longrightarrow 2\,NaCl(aq) + H_2CO_3(aq)$$

Bubbles of a colorless gas are evolved when these solutions are mixed. Although this gas is evidence of a chemical reaction, neither of the indicated products is a gas. But carbonic acid, H_2CO_3, is an unstable compound and readily decomposes into carbon dioxide and water.

$$H_2CO_3(aq) \longrightarrow H_2O(l) + CO_2(g)$$

Therefore, CO_2 and H_2O are the products that should be written in the equation. The original equation then becomes

$$Na_2CO_3(aq) + 2\,HCl(aq) \longrightarrow 2\,NaCl(aq) + H_2O(l) + CO_2(g)$$

The evolution of a gas is indicated by a (g).

Examples of some other substances that decompose to form gases are sulfurous acid (H_2SO_3) and ammonium hydroxide (NH_4OH):

$$H_2SO_3(aq) \longrightarrow H_2O(l) + SO_2(g)$$
$$NH_4OH(aq) \longrightarrow H_2O(l) + NH_3(g)$$

Example 4. When solutions of sodium hydroxide and hydrochloric acid are mixed, the equation for the double displacement reaction (hypothetical) is

$$NaOH(aq) + HCl(aq) \longrightarrow NaCl(aq) + H_2O(l)$$

The mixture of these solutions produces no visible evidence of reaction, but on touching the test tube we notice that it feels warm. The evolution of heat is evidence of a chemical reaction. **Example 4** and **Example 1** appear similar because there is no visible evidence of reaction. However, the difference is very important. In **Example 1** all four ions are still uncombined. In **Example 4** the hydrogen ions (H^+) and hydroxide ions (OH^-) are no longer free in solution but have combined to form water. The reaction of H^+ (an acid) and OH^- (a base) is called **neutralization.** The formation of the slightly ionized compound (water) caused the reaction to occur and was the source of the heat liberated.

Water is the most common slightly ionized substance formed in double displacement reactions; other examples are acetic acid ($HC_2H_3O_2$), oxalic acid ($H_2C_2O_4$), and phosphoric acid (H_3PO_4).

From the four examples cited we see that a double displacement reaction will occur if at least one of the following classes of substances is formed by the reaction:

1. A precipitate

2. A gas

3. A slightly ionized compound, usually water

PROCEDURE

Wear protective glasses.

Each part of the experiment (except No. 12) consists of mixing equal volumes of two solutions in a test tube. Use about a **3 mL sample** of each solution (about 1.5 cm of liquid in a standard test tube). It is not necessary to measure each volume accurately. Record your observations at the time of mixing. Where there is no visible evidence of reaction, feel each tube, or check with a thermometer, to determine if heat is evolved (exothermic reaction). In each case where a reaction has occurred, complete and balance the equation, properly indicating precipitates and gases. When there is no evidence of reaction, write the words "No reaction" as the right-hand side of the equation.

1. Mix 0.1 M sodium chloride and 0.1 M potassium nitrate solutions.

2. Mix 0.1 M sodium chloride and 0.1 M silver nitrate solutions.

3. Mix 0.1 M sodium carbonate and **dilute** (6 M) hydrochloric acid solutions.

4. Mix 10 percent sodium hydroxide and dil. (6 M) hydrochloric acid solutions.

5. Mix 0.1 M barium chloride and dil. (3 M) sulfuric acid solutions.

 6. Mix **dilute** (6 M) ammonium hydroxide and **dilute** (3 M) sulfuric acid solutions.

7. Mix 0.1 M copper(II) sulfate and 0.1 M zinc nitrate solutions.

8. Mix 0.1 M sodium carbonate and 0.1 M calcium chloride solutions.

9. Mix 0.1 M copper(II) sulfate and 0.1 M ammonium chloride solutions.

10. Mix 10 percent sodium hydroxide and dil. (6 M) nitric acid solutions.

11. Mix 0.1 M iron(III) chloride and dil. (6 M) ammonium hydroxide solutions.

 12. **Do this part in the fume hood.** Add 1 g of solid sodium sulfite to 3 mL of water and shake to dissolve. Now add about 1 mL of conc. (12 M) hydrochloric acid solution, a drop at a time, using a medicine dropper. Observe the results carefully.

 Dispose of mixtures from reactions 2, 5, 7, 9 in the "heavy metal waste" container. Dispose of the contents of reaction 12 in the sink inside the hood. Dispose of the contents of all other tubes in the sink and flush with water.

REPORT FOR EXPERIMENT 11

Double Displacement Reactions

$$AB + CD \rightarrow CB + AD$$

Directions for completing table below:

1. Record your observations (Evidence of Reaction) of each experiment. Use the following terminology: (a) "Precipitate formed" (include the color), (b) "Gas evolved," (c) "Heat evolved," or (d) "No reaction observed."

2. Complete and balance the equation for each case in which a reaction occurred. First write the correct formulas for the products, taking into account the charges (oxidation numbers) of the ions involved. Then balance the equation by placing a whole number in front of each formula (as needed) to adjust the number of atoms of each element so that they are the same on both sides of the equation. Use (g) or (s) to indicate gases and precipitates. Where no evidence of reaction was observed, write the words "No reaction" as the right-hand side of the equation.

Evidence of Reactions	Balanced Equations
1. no change	$NaCl_{(aq)} + KNO_{3(aq)} \rightarrow$ NR
2. turns milky white (ppt)	$NaCl_{(aq)} + AgNO_{3(aq)} \rightarrow AgCl_{(s)} + NaNO_{3(aq)}$
3. forms a gas	$Na_2CO_{3(aq)} + 2HCl_{(aq)} \rightarrow 2NaCl_{(aq)} + CO_{2(g)} + H_2O_{(l)}$
4. temperature changed	$NaOH_{(aq)} + HCl_{(aq)} \rightarrow NaCl_{(aq)} + H_2O_{(l)}$
5. turns milky white	$BaCl_{2(aq)} + H_2SO_{4(aq)} \rightarrow BaSO_{4(s)} + HCl_{(aq)}$
6. temperature changed	$NH_4OH_{(aq)} + H_2SO_{4(aq)} \rightarrow (NH_4)_2SO_{4(aq)} + H_2O_{(l)}$
7. no change	$CuSO_{4(aq)} + Zn(NO_3)_{2(aq)} \nrightarrow$ NR
8. turns milky white	$Na_2CO_{3(aq)} + CaCl_{2(aq)} \rightarrow 2NaCl_{(aq)} + CaCO_{3(s)}$
9. no change	$CuSO_{4(aq)} + NH_4Cl_{(aq)} \nrightarrow$ NR
10. temperature changed	$NaOH_{(aq)} + HNO_3 \rightarrow NaNO_{3(aq)} + H_2O_{(l)}$
11. dark brown (ppt)	$FeCl_{3(aq)} + NH_4OH_{(aq)} \rightarrow Fe(OH)_{2(s)} + NH_4Cl_{(aq)}$
12. forms a gas	$Na_2SO_{3(aq)} + HCl_{(aq)} \rightarrow NaCl + H_2O_{(l)} + CO_{2(g)}$

QUESTIONS AND PROBLEMS

1. The formation of what three classes of substances caused double displacement reactions to occur in this experiment?

   (a) formation of a gas (the product of the reaction had a gaseous form).

   (b) neutralization formation (during an acid-base reaction, formed a salt & water)

   (c) formation of a precipitate (a solid is formed in a solution)

2. Write the equation for the decomposition of sulfurous acid.

   $$H_2SO_{3(aq)} \rightleftharpoons H_2O_{(\ell)} + SO_{2(g)}$$

3. Using three criteria for double displacement reactions, together with the Solubility Table in Appendix 5, predict whether a double displacement reaction will occur in each example below. If reaction will occur, complete and balance the equation, properly indicating gases and precipitates. If you believe no reaction will occur, write "no reaction" as the right-hand side of the equation. All reactants are in aqueous solution.

   (a) $K_2S_{(aq)} + CuSO_{4(aq)} \longrightarrow K_2SO_{4(aq)} + CuS_{(s)}$

   (b) $2\,NH_4OH_{(aq)} + H_2C_2O_{4(aq)} \longrightarrow (NH_4)_2C_2O_{4(aq)} + 2H_2O_{(\ell)}$

   (c) $KOH_{(aq)} + NH_4Cl_{(aq)} \xrightarrow{\Delta} KCl_{(aq)} + H_2O_{(\ell)} + NH_{3(g)}$

   (d) $NaC_2H_3O_{2(aq)} + HCl_{(aq)} \longrightarrow HC_2H_3O_{2(aq)} + NaCl_{(aq)}$

   (e) $2\,Na_2CrO_{4(aq)} + Pb(C_2H_3O_2)_{2(aq)} \longrightarrow Pb(CrO_4)_{2(s)} + 2NaC_2H_3O_{2(aq)}$

   (f) $(NH_4)_2SO_{4(aq)} + 2NaCl_{(aq)} \longrightarrow Na_2SO_{4(aq)} + NH_{3(g)} + 2HCl_{(aq)}$

   (g) $BiCl_{3(aq)} + 3NaOH_{(aq)} \longrightarrow 3NaCl_{ppt} + Bi(OH)_3$

   (h) $KC_2H_3O_2 + CoSO_4 \longrightarrow NR$

   (i) $Na_2CO_{3(aq)} + 2HNO_{3(aq)} \longrightarrow 2NaNO_{3(aq)} + H_2O_{(\ell)} + CO_{2(g)}$

   (j) $3\,ZnBr_{2(aq)} + 2\,K_3PO_{4(aq)} \longrightarrow Zn_3(PO_4)_{2(s)\ ppt} + 6KBr_{(aq)}$

EXPERIMENT 12

Single Displacement Reactions

MATERIALS AND EQUIPMENT

Solids: strips of sheet copper, lead, and zinc measuring about 1×2 cm; and sandpaper or emery cloth. **Solutions:** 0.1 M copper(II) nitrate [$Cu(NO_3)_2$], 0.1 M lead(II) nitrate [$Pb(NO_3)_2$], 0.1 M magnesium sulfate ($MgSO_4$), 0.1 M silver nitrate ($AgNO_3$), and dilute (3 M) sulfuric acid (H_2SO_4). Small test tubes.

DISCUSSION

The chemical reactivity of elements varies over an immense range. Some, like sodium and fluorine, are so reactive that they are never found in the free or uncombined state in nature. Others, like xenon and platinum, are nearly inert and can be made to react with other elements only under special conditions.

The **reactivity** of an element is related to its tendency to lose or gain electrons; that is, to be oxidized or reduced. In principle it is possible to arrange nearly all the elements into a single series in order of their reactivities. A series of this kind indicates which free elements are capable of displacing other elements from their compounds. Such a list is known as an **activity** or **electromotive series.** To illustrate the preparation of an activity series, we will experiment with a small group of selected elements and their compounds.

A generalized single displacement reaction is represented by the equation

$$A(s) + BC(aq) \longrightarrow B(s) + AC(aq)$$

Element A is the more active element and replaces element B from the compound BC. But if element B is more active than element A, no reaction will occur.

Let us consider two specific examples, using copper and mercury.

Example 1. A few drops of mercury metal are added to a solution of copper(II) chloride ($CuCl_2$).

Example 2. A strip of metallic copper is immersed in a solution of mercury(II) chloride ($HgCl_2$).

In Example 1 no change is observed even after the solution has been standing for a prolonged time, and we conclude that there is no reaction. In Example 2 the copper strip is soon coated with metallic mercury, and the solution becomes pale green. From this evidence we conclude that mercury will not displace copper in copper compounds but copper will displace mercury in mercury compounds. Therefore copper is a more reactive metal than mercury and is above mercury in the activity series. In terms of chemical equations these facts may be represented as

EXPERIMENT 13

Ionization-Electrolytes and pH

MATERIALS AND EQUIPMENT

Demonstration. **Solids:** sodium chloride (NaCl) and sugar ($C_{12}H_{22}O_{11}$). **Liquid:** glacial acetic acid ($HC_2H_3O_2$). **Solutions:** 0.1 M ammonium chloride (NH_4Cl), 1 M ammonium hydroxide (NH_4OH), 1 M acetic acid ($HC_2H_3O_2$), saturated barium hydroxide [$Ba(OH)_2$], 0.1 M copper(II) sulfate ($CuSO_4$), 1 M hydrochloric acid (HCl), 0.1 M nickel(II) nitrate [$Ni(NO_3)_2$], 0.1 M sodium bromide (NaBr), 1 M sodium hydroxide (NaOH), 0.1 M sodium nitrate ($NaNO_3$), and dilute (3 M) sulfuric acid (H_2SO_4). Conductivity apparatus; magnetic stirrer and stirring bar.

Solids: calcium hydroxide [$Ca(OH)_2$], calcium oxide (CaO), iron wire (paper clips), magnesium ribbon (Mg), magnesium oxide (MgO), marble chips ($CaCO_3$), sodium bicarbonate ($NaHCO_3$), sulfur (S), and wood splints. **Solutions:** dilute (6 M) acetic acid ($HC_2H_3O_2$), dilute (6 M) ammonium hydroxide (NH_4OH), dilute (6 M) hydrochloric acid (HCl), dilute (6 M) nitric acid (HNO_3), phenolphthalein, 10 percent sodium hydroxide (NaOH), and dilute (3 M) sulfuric acid (H_2SO_4). 0.001 M HCl, 0.01 M HCl, 0.1 M HCl for pH measurements, pH meter.

DISCUSSION

A. Electrolytes

Pure water will not conduct an electric current. However, when many solutes are dissolved in water, the resulting aqueous solutions will conduct electricity. These solutes, called **electrolytes,** form ions which are free to move in the solution. The electrical current through the solution is the movement of these ions to the positive and negative electrodes. Electrolytes are **acids, bases, and salts,** depending on the ions in solution. Other substances such as sugar and alcohol dissolve in water but are nonconductors because they do not form ions and are called **nonelectrolytes**.

The ions in an aqueous electrolyte solution are the result of the **dissociation** or **ionization** of compounds in water. Compounds that dissociate or ionize in water are **acids, bases and salts.** For example:

Dissociation of NaOH (a base) and NaCl (a salt):

$$NaOH(s) \xrightarrow{H_2O} Na^+(aq) + OH^-(aq)$$

$$NaCl(s) \xrightarrow{H_2O} Na^+(aq) + Cl^-(aq)$$

Ionization of HCl (a strong acid) and $HC_2H_3O_2$ (a weak acid)

$$HCl(g) + H_2O(l) \longrightarrow H_3O^+(aq) + Cl^-(aq)$$

$$HC_2H_3O_2(l) + H_2O(l) \rightleftharpoons H_3O^+(aq) + C_2H_3O_2^-(aq)$$

The necessity for water in this ionization process is illustrated by the fact that, when hydrogen chloride is dissolved in benzene, no ions are formed and the solution is a nonconductor (nonelectrolyte).

Electrolytes are classifed as strong or weak depending on the extent to which they exist as ions in solutions. **Strong electrolytes** are essentially 100 percent ionized in water, that is they exist totally as ions in solution. **Weak electrolytes** are considerably less ionized, only a small amount of the dissolved substance exists as ions, the remainder being in the un-ionized or molecular from. Most salts are strong electrolytes; acids and bases occur as both strong and weak electrolytes. Examples are as follows:

Strong Electrolytes	**Weak Electrolytes**
Most salts	$HC_2H_3O_2$
HCl	H_2SO_3
H_2SO_4	HNO_2
HNO_3	H_2CO_3
NaOH	H_2S
KOH	$H_2C_2O_4$
$Ba(OH)_2$	H_3PO_4
$Ca(OH)_2$	NH_4OH

In the first part of this experiment, the conductivity of many aqueous solutions will be demonstrated.

B. Acids

1. **Acids** are described as substances that yield hydrogen ions (H^+) when dissolved in water. This definition was first proposed by the Swedish chemist Arrhenius (over 100 years ago) for electrolytes which share common properties such as sour taste and the ability to change the color of the plant dye, litmus to red. This definition is the simplest way to think of acids and still applies.

Many compounds can be recognized as acids from their written formulas. The ionizable hydrogen atoms, which are responsible for the acidity, are written first, followed by the symbols of the other elements in the formula. Examples are:

HCl	Hydrochloric acid	H_2CO_3	Carbonic acid
HNO_3	Nitric Acid	HNO_2	Nitrous acid
H_2SO_4	Sulfuric Acid	H_2SO_3	Sulfurous Acid
$HC_2H_3O_2$	Acetic Acid	$H_2C_2O_4$	Oxalic Acid
H_3PO_4	Phosphoric Acid		

Acids are formed by the reaction of nonmetallic oxides called **acid anhydrides** with water. For example:

$$SO_3(g) + H_2O(l) \longrightarrow H_2SO_4(aq)$$

The chemical properties of acids will be observed in Procedure B.

2. **Bronsted-Lowry Acids and Bases**

The more inclusive Bronsted-Lowry acid-base theory defines acids as proton (H^+) donors and bases as proton acceptors. Thus, water behaves as both an acid and a base, as illustrated by the equation:

$$H_2O + H_2O \rightleftharpoons H_3O^+ + OH^-$$
$$\text{acid} \quad \text{base} \qquad \text{acid} \quad \text{base}$$

One water molecule has donated a proton, H^+, (acted as an acid) and another water molecule has accepted a proton (acted as a base). The hydronium ion, H_3O^+, is a hydrated hydrogen ion (H^+H_2O). To simplify writing equations, the formula of the hydronium ion is often abbreviated H^+. However, free hydrogen ions do not actually exist in aqueous solutions.

C. Bases

The Arrhenius definition for **bases** describes them as substances that yield hydroxide ions ($OH-$) in water solutions. Bases change the color of litmus to blue. Common bases can be recognized by their formulas as a hydroxide ion (OH^-) combined with a metal or other positive ion. Examples are:

NaOH	Sodium hydroxide	KOH	Potassium hydroxide
$Ca(OH)_2$	Calcium hydroxide	$Mg(OH)_2$	Magnesium hydroxide
NH_4OH	Ammonium hydroxide		

The terms **alkali** and **alkaline** solutions are used synonymously with base and basic solutions.

Metal oxides that react with water to form bases are **basic anhydrides.** For example:

$$CaO(s) + H_2O(l) \longrightarrow Ca(OH)_2(aq)$$

The physical and chemical properties of bases will be observed in Procedure C.

D. Salts

Salts consist of a positively charged ion (H^+ excluded) and a negatively charged ion (O^{2-} and OH^- excluded). Salts may be formed by the reaction of acids and bases, or by replacing the hydrogen atoms in an acid with a metal, or by interaction of two other salts. There are many more salts than acids and bases. For example, for a single acid such as HCl we can produce many chloride salts (e.g. NaCl, KCl, RbCl, $CaCl_2$, NH_4Cl, $FeCl_3$, etc.)

The reaction of an acid and a base to form water and a salt is known as **neutralization.** For example:

$$HCl(aq) + NaOH(aq) \longrightarrow H_2O(l) + NaCl(aq)$$

E. The Importance and Measurement of H^+ Ion Concentration

An aqueous solution will be acidic, basic, or neutral, depending on the relative concentrations of H^+ and OH^-. In acidic solutions the concentration of the H^+ ions is greater than that of the OH^- ions. In basic solutions the concentration of the OH^- ions is greater than that of the H^+ ions. If the concentrations of H^+ and OH^- are equal (as in water), the solution is **neutral.**

There are two general methods for determining the relative concentrations of H^+ and OH^- and thus whether a solution is acid, alkaline, or neutral.

1. **Indicators** are organic compounds that change color at a particular hydrogen or hydroxide ion concentration. For example, litmus, a vegetable dye, shows a pink color in acidic solutions and a blue color in alkaline solutions. Another common indicator is phenolphthalein; it is colorless in acid solutions and pink in basic solutions. An indicator can only determine the relative concentrations of H^+ and OH^- within the range of its color changes.

2. A **pH meter** is an instrument designed so that it measures the H^+ directly and is used when an accurate measurement of the concentration of H^+ is needed. The pH meter is described and explained more fully in section (F).

F. Measuring pH

The H^+ ion has a great effect on many chemical reactions, including biological processes that sustain life. For example, the H^+ concentration of human blood is regulated to very close tolerances. The concentration of this important ion is expressed as pH rather than other concentration expressions such as molarity. The pH is defined by this formula:

$$pH = -\log[H^+]$$

The H^+ written in brackets $[H^+]$ represents the concentration of H^+ in moles/liter. The logarithm (log) of a number is simply the power to which 10 must be raised to give that number. Thus, the log of 0.001 is -3 ($0.001 = 10^{-3}$). Since pH is defined as the negative log of an $[H^+]$ value, then the pH of a solution with $[H^+] = 0.001$ moles/liter is $-(-3)$ or pH = 3.

The pH of pure water is 7.0 at 25°C and is said to be neutral, that is, it is neither acidic nor basic because $[H^+]$ and $[OH^-]$ are equal (10^{-7} moles/liter). Solutions that are acidic have pH values less than 7.0. Solution that are basic have pH values greater than 7.0.

pH < 7.0	acid solutions
pH = 7.0	neutral solutions
pH > 7.0	basic (alkaline) solutions

A pH meter is a delicate instrument that comes in many versions and sizes which share some of these common features.

1. pH meters use a glass electrode that is immersed in the solution being tested. The electrode converts the H^+ concentration into an electrical potential which is read by a voltmeter calibrated in pH units.

2. pH meters are calibrated against standard solutions of known pH. After calibration, the electrode is immersed in the test solutions and the pH meter provides a value relative to the standard.

3. The operation of pH meters varies with different models. Your instructor will demonstrate the use of the pH meter available to you.

PROCEDURE

Wear protective glasses.

A. Conductivity of Solutions—Instructor Demonstration

All of the following tests (except number 8) are performed in 18 × 150 mm test tubes, using the conductivity apparatus shown in Figure 13.1 or other suitable conductivity apparatus. The electrodes should be rinsed thoroughly with distilled water between the testing of different solutions.

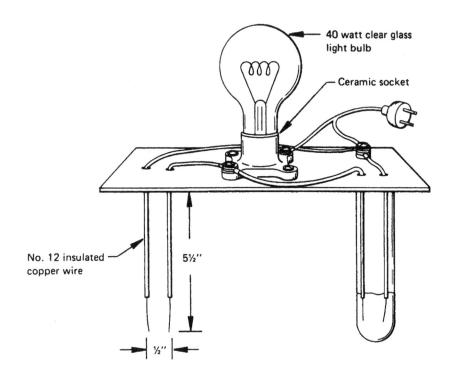

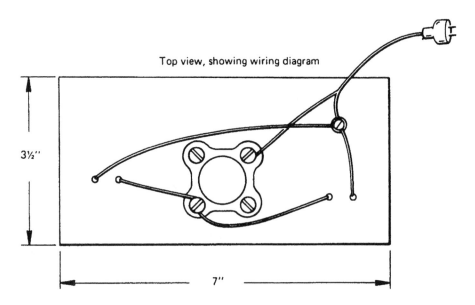

Figure 13.1 Conductivity apparatus

Each test is performed by filling a test tube about half full of the liquid to be tested, then raising the test tube up around a pair of electrodes. When a measurable number of ions are in solution, the solution will conduct the electric current and the light will glow. A dimly glowing light indicates a relatively small number of ions in solution; a brightly glowing light indicates a relatively large number of ions in solution.

NOTE: The student should complete the data table in the report form at the time the demonstration is performed.

---

1. Test the conductivity of distilled water.

2. Test the conductivity of tap water.

3. Add a small amount of sugar to a test tube that is half full of distilled water. Dissolve the sugar and test the solution for conductivity.

4. Add a small amount of sodium chloride to a test tube that is half full of distilled water. Dissolve the salt and test the solution for conductivity.

 5. Remove the plug from the electrical outlet, clean and dry the electrodes, and reconnect the plug.

(a) Test the conductivity of glacial acetic acid.

(b) Pour out half of the acid, replace with distilled water, mix, and test the solution for conductivity.

(c) Pour out half of the solution in 5(b), replace with distilled water, mix, and test the solution for conductivity.

6. Strong and weak acids and bases. Test the following 1 molar solutions for conductivity: (a) acetic acid, (b) hydrochloric acid, (c) ammonium hydroxide, (d) sodium hydroxide. If the conductivity apparatus has two sets of electrodes, as shown in Figure 13.1, the relative conductivity of the strong and weak acids or bases may be compared by alternately raising a tube of each solution around the electrodes. Clean and dry the electrodes (See No. 5).

7. Test the following 0.1 M salt solutions for conductivity: (a) sodium nitrate, (b) sodium bromide, (c) nickel(II) nitrate, (d) copper(II) sulfate, and (e) ammonium chloride.

8. Clean the electrodes well. Place about 25 mL of distilled water and 1 drop of dil. (3 M) sulfuric acid in a 150 mL beaker. Place the beaker on a magnetic stirrer and dip one set of electrodes into the solution. With the stirrer slowly turning, add saturated barium hydroxide solution dropwise until the light goes out completely. Add a few more milliliters of barium hydroxide solution.

B. Properties of Acids

 Dispose of all solutions in the sink and flush with water. Take care to make sure that solids such as metal strips, splints, and unreacted marble chips do not go into the sink. They should be put into the wastebasket.

1. **Reaction with a Metal**

   (a) Into four consecutive test tubes place about 5 mL of dil. (6 M) hydrochloric, (3 M) sulfuric, (6 M) nitric, and (6 M) acetic acids.

   (b) Place a small strip of magnesium ribbon into each tube, one at a time, and test the gas evolved for hydrogen by bringing a burning splint to the mouth of the tube. If the liberation of gas is slow, stopper the test tube loosely for a minute or two before testing for hydrogen.

2. **Measurement of Acidity and pH**

   (a) Test dilute solutions of hydrochloric acid, acetic acid, and sulfuric acid by placing a drop of each acid from a stirring rod onto a strip of red and onto a strip of blue litmus paper. Note any color changes.

   (b) Add 2 drops of phenolphthalein solution to about 5 mL of distilled water. Add several drops of dilute hydrochloric acid, mix, and note any color change.

   (c) Use the pH meter to measure the pH of three dilutions of hydrochloric acid in this order: 0.001 M HCl, 0.01 M HCl, and 0.1 M HCl. *Rinse the electrodes thoroughly with distilled water when done.*

3. **Reaction with Carbonates and Bicarbonates**

   (a) Cover the bottom of a 150 mL beaker with a small quantity of sodium bicarbonate powder. Now add about 4 to 5 mL of dil. (6 M) hydrochloric acid to the beaker and cover with a glass plate. After about 30 seconds lower a burning splint into the beaker and observe the results. Dispose of the reaction mixture in the sink.

   (b) Repeat the above experiment, using a few granules of marble chips (calcium carbonate) instead of sodium bicarbonate. Allow the reaction to proceed for 2 minutes before testing with the burning splint. Dispose of unreacted marble chips in the wastebasket, not the sink.

4. **Reaction with Bases—Neutralization.** To about 25 mL of water in a beaker, add 3 drops of phenolphthalein solution and 5 drops of dil. (6 M) hydrochloric acid. Using a medicine dropper, add 10 percent sodium hydroxide solution dropwise, stirring after each drop, until the indicator in the solution changes color. Then add dilute hydrochloric acid, drop by drop, stirring after each drop, until the indicator becomes colorless again. Repeat the additions of base and acid one or two more times. Dispose of all solutions in the sink.

5. **Nonmetal Oxide plus Water** Dispose of all solutions in the sink.

   (a) **Do this part in the fume hood.** Place a small lump of sulfur in a deflagrating spoon and start it burning by heating in the burner flame. Lower the burning sulfur into a wide-mouth bottle containing 15 mL of distilled water and let the sulfur burn for 2 minutes. Remove the deflagrating spoon and quench the excess burning sulfur in a beaker of water. Cover the bottle with a glass plate and shake the bottle back and forth to dissolve the sulfur dioxide gas. Test the solution with blue litmus paper.

   (b) As shown in Figure 13.2, fit a test tube with a one-hole stopper containing a glass delivery tube long enough to extend to the bottom of another test tube. Place several pieces of marble chips and a few milliliters of dil. (6 M) hydrochloric acid into the tube and insert the stopper. Bubble the liberated carbon dioxide into another test tube containing 10 mL water, 1 drop of 10 percent sodium hydroxide solution, and 2 drops of phenolphthalein solution. Record the results.

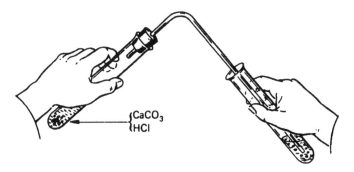

Figure 13.2   Generator for carbon dioxide

C.   Properties of Bases

 Dispose of all solutions in the sink.

1. "Feel" Test. Make very dilute solutions by adding 5 drops of dilute (6 M) ammonium hydroxide to 10 mL of water in a test tube and 3 drops of 10 percent sodium hydroxide solution to 10 mL of water in another test tube. Rub a small amount of each very dilute solution between your fingers to obtain the characteristic "feel" of a hydroxide (base) solution. Wash your hands thoroughly immediately after making the "feel" test. Save the very dilute base solutions for the measurement of pH in the next section, C2(c).

2. **Measurement of Alkalinity**

   (a) Test the two base (alkaline) solutions prepared in C.1 with both red and blue litmus paper. Note any color changes.

   (b) Add 2 drops of phenolphthalein solution to each of the two alkaline solutions prepared in C.1. Note any color changes.

   (c) Pour the dilute ammonium hydroxide and sodium hydroxide that were prepared in the previous step into separate small beakers. Use the pH meter to measure the pH of these alkaline solutions. *Dip the electrode in dilute acetic acid and rinse thoroughly with distilled water when done.*

3. **Metal Oxides plus Water**

   (a) Place 10 mL of water and 2 drops of phenolphthalein solution in each of 3 test tubes. Add a pinch of calcium oxide to the first, magnesium oxide to the second, and calcium hydroxide to the third tube. Note and record the results.

   (b) Wind the end of a 5 cm piece of iron wire (or paper clip) around a small marble chip. Grasp the wire with tongs and heat the marble chip in the hottest part of the burner (flame for about 2 minutes—the edges of the chip should become white hot while being heated. Allow the chip to cool; then drop it into a beaker containing 15 mL of water and 2 drops of phenolphthalein solution. For comparison, repeat this part of the experiment with a marble chip which has not been heated. Note the results. **Return the iron wire to the reagent shelf.** Dispose marble chips in the wastebasket.

4. **Reaction with Acids—Neutralization.** Review Part B.4.

REPORT FOR EXPERIMENT 13

Ionization—Electrolytes and pH

A. Conductivity of Solutions—Instructor Demonstration

Complete the table for each of the substances tested in the ionization demonstration. Place an "X" in the column where the property of the substance tested fits the column description.

	Nonelectrolyte	Strong Electrolyte	Weak Electrolyte
1. Distilled Water			
2. Tap water			
3. Sugar			
4. NaCl			
5. a. $HC_2H_3O_2$ (glacial)			
b. 1st dilution			
c. 2nd dilution			
6. a. 1 M $HC_2H_3O_2$			
b. 1 M HCl			
c. 1 M NH_4OH			
d. 1 M NaOH			
7. a. $NaNO_3$			
b. NaBr			
c. $Ni(NO_3)_2$			
d. $CuSO_4$			
e. NH_4Cl			

8. (a) Write an equation for the chemical reaction that occurred between sulfuric acid and barium hydroxide.

(b) Explain in terms of the properties of the products formed why the light went out when barium hydroxide was added to sulfuric acid solution, even though both of these reactants are electrolytes.

(c) Explain why the light came on again when additional barium hydroxide was added.

9. In the conductivity tests, what controlled the brightness of the light?

10. Write an equation to show how acetic acid reacts with water to produce ions in solution.

11. What classes of compounds tested are electrolytes?

B.   Properties of Acids

1. **Reaction with a Metal**

(a) Write the formulas of the acids which liberated hydrogen gas when reacting with magnesium metal.

_____

(b) Write equations to represent the reactions in which hydrogen gas was formed.

2. **Measurement of Acidity and pH**

   (a) What is the effect of acids on the color of red litmus?

   (b) What is the effect of acids on the color of blue litmus?

   (c) What color is phenolphthalein in an acid solution?   _____

   (d) What was the pH of the hydrochloric acids tested?

      0.001 M _____   0.01 M _____   0.1 M _____

   (e) Which pH measured has the highest number of H^+ in solution?   _____

   (f) What is the H^+ concentration in an acid with of pH 4.6?
   Express your answer as a power of 10   _____

      Refer to Study Aid 4 if you need help with using your calculator to convert the pH
   into H^+ concentration using the antilog function.

3. **Reaction with Carbonates and Bicarbonates**

   (a) What gas is formed in these reactions?

      Name _____   Formula _____

   (b) What happened to the burning splint when it was thrust into the beaker?

   (c) What do you conclude about one of the properties of the gas in the beaker, based on
   the behavior of the burning splint?

   (d) Complete and balance the equations representing the reactions:

   $$NaHCO_3(s) + HCl(aq) \longrightarrow$$

   $$CaCO_3(s) + \quad HCl(aq) \longrightarrow$$

4. **Reaction of Acids with Bases—Neutralization**

(a) Write an equation for the neutralization reaction of HCl and NaOH.

(b) How did you know when all the acid was neutralized?

5. **Nonmetal Oxide plus Water**

(a) Write an equation for the combustion of sulfur in air.

(b) What acid is formed when the product of the sulfur combustion reacts with water?

Name _____   Formula _____

Write the equation for its formation.

(c) What evidence in this experiment leads you to believe that carbon dioxide in water has acidic properties?

(d) What acid is formed when carbon dioxide reacts with water?

Name _____   Formula _____

C. **Properties of Bases**

1. **"Feel" Test.** What is the characteristic feel of basic solutions?

2. **Measurement of Alkalinity**

(a) What is the effect of bases on the color of red litmus?

(b) What is the effect of bases on the color of blue litmus?

(c) What color is phenolphthalein in a basic solution?   _____

(d) What was the pH for each dilute base tested?

   $NH_4OH(aq)$ _____ $NaOH(aq)$ _____

(e) Which base tested has the highest number of H^+ in solution?   _____

(f) What is the H^+ concentration in the strongest base tested?
   Express your answer as a power of 10.   _____

   Refer to Study Aid 4 if you need help using your calculator to convert the pH into H^+
   concentration using the antilog function.

3. Metal Oxides plus Water

(a.1) Color (if any) produced by phenolphthalein.

                                        Color with CaO in water   _____

                                        Color with MgO in water   _____

                                        Color with $Ca(OH)_2$ in water   _____

(a.2) Complete and balance these equations:

   $CaO(s) +$ $H_2O(l) \longrightarrow$

   $MgO(s) +$ $H_2O(l) \longrightarrow$

(b.1) The formula for marble is $CaCO_3$, What compounds are formed when it is heated
   strongly?

(b.2) Write the equation representing this decomposition:

   $CaCO_3(s) \overset{\Delta}{\longrightarrow}$

(b.3) What evidence led you to formulate the composition of the solid residue after heating the marble chip?

ADDITIONAL QUESTIONS AND PROBLEMS

1. State whether each of the formulas below represents an **acid,** a **base,** a **salt,** an **acid anhydride,** a **basic anhydride,** or **none** of these types of compounds:

CuF_2 _____ $CaSO_4$ _____

$Ba(OH)_2$ _____ C_2H_4 _____

$LiOH$ _____ $C_{12}H_{22}O_{11}$ _____

$HBrO_3$ _____ HI _____

$RaCO_3$ _____ P_2O_5 _____

KNO_2 _____ HCN _____

$H_2C_2O_4$ _____ MgO _____

2. Complete and balance the following equations and name the product formed. (Only one product is formed in each case.)

Name of Product

(a) $K_2O(s) +$ $H_2O(l) \longrightarrow$ _____

(b) $SrO(s) +$ $H_2O(l) \longrightarrow$ _____

(c) $SO_3(s) +$ $H_2O(l) \longrightarrow$ _____

(d) $N_2O_5(s) +$ $H_2O(l) \longrightarrow$ _____

EXPERIMENT 14

Identification of Selected Anions

MATERIALS AND EQUIPMENT

Liquids: Decane ($C_{10}H_{22}$). **Solutions:** 0.1 M barium chloride ($BaCl_2$), freshly prepared chlorine water (Cl_2), dilute (6 M) hydrochloric acid (HCl), dilute (6 M) nitric acid (HNO_3), 0.1 M silver nitrate ($AgNO_3$), 0.1 M sodium bromide (NaBr), 0.1 M sodium carbonate (Na_2CO_3), 0.1 M sodium chloride (NaCl), 0.1 M sodium iodide (NaI), 0.1 M sodium phosphate (Na_3PO_4), 0.1 M sodium sulfate (Na_2SO_4), and unknown solutions. Wash bottle for distilled water.

DISCUSSION

The examination of a sample of inorganic material to identify the ions that are present is called **qualitative analysis.** To introduce qualitative analysis, we will analyze for six anions (negatively charged ions). The ions selected for identification are chloride (Cl^-), bromide (Br^-), iodide (I^-), sulfate ($SO_4{}^{2-}$), phosphate ($PO_4{}^{3-}$) and carbonate ($CO_3{}^{2-}$).

Qualitative analysis is based on the fact that no two ions behave identically in all of their chemical reactions. Identification depends on appropriate chemical tests coupled with careful observation of such characteristics as solution color, formation and color of precipitates, evolution of gases, etc. Test reactions are selected to identify the ions in the fewest steps possible. In this experiment only one anion is assumed to be present in each sample. If two or more anions must be detected in a single solution, the scheme of analysis can be considerably more complex.

Silver Nitrate Test

When solutions of the sodium salts of the six anions are reacted with silver nitrate solution, the following precipitates are formed: AgCl, AgBr, AgI, Ag_3PO_4, and Ag_2CO_3. Ag_2SO_4 is moderately soluble and does not precipitate at the concentrations used in these solutions. When dilute nitric acid is added, the precipitates Ag_3PO_4, and Ag_2CO_3 dissolve; AgCl, AgBr, and AgI remain undissolved. Acids react with carbonates to form CO_2 (g). Look for gas bubbles when nitric acid is added to the silver precipitates.

In some cases a tentative identification of an anion may be made from the silver nitrate test. This identification is based on the color of the precipitate and on whether or not the precipitate is soluble in nitric acid. However, since two or more anions may give similar results, second or third confirmatory tests are necessary for positive identification.

Barium Chloride Test

When barium chloride solution is added to solutions of the sodium salts of the six anions, precipitates of $BaSO_4$, $Ba_3(PO_4)_2$ and $BaCO_3$, are obtained. No precipitate is obtained with Cl^-, Br^-, or I^-.

When dilute hydrochloric acid is added, the precipitates $Ba_3(PO_4)_2$ and $BaCO_3$ dissolve; $BaSO_4$ does not dissolve. Look for CO_2 gas bubbles.

Organic Solvent Test

The silver nitrate test can prove the presence of a halide ion (Cl^-, Br^-, or I^-) because the silver precipitates of the other three anions dissolve in nitric acid. But the colors of the three silver halides do not differ sufficiently to establish which halide ion is present.

Adding chlorine water (Cl_2 dissolved in water) to halide salts in solution will oxidize bromide ion to free bromine (Br_2) and iodine ion to free iodine (I_2). The free halogen may be extracted from the water solution by adding an immiscible organic solvent such as decane and shaking vigorously. The colors of the three halogens in organic solvents are quite different. Cl_2 is pale yellow, Br_2 is yellow-orange to reddish-brown, and I_2 is pink to violet. After adding chlorine water and shaking, a yellow-orange to reddish-brown color in the decane layer indicates that Br^- was present in the original solution; a pink to violet color in the decane layer indicates that I^- was present. However, a pale yellow color does not indicate Cl^-, since Cl_2 was added as a reagent. But if the silver nitrate test gives a white precipitate that is insoluble in nitric acid, and the organic solvent test shows no Br^- or I^-, then you can conclude that Cl^- was present.

Though we have described many of the expected results of these tests, it is necessary to test known solutions to actually see the results of the tests and to develop satisfactory experimental techniques. During this experiment, you will perform these tests on six known anions.

Then, two "unknown" solutions, each containing one of the six anions, will be analyzed. When an unknown is analyzed, the results should agree in all respects with one of the known anions. If the results do not fully agree with one of the six known ions, either the testing has been poorly done or the unknown does not contain any of the specified ions.

Three different kinds of equations may be used to express the behavior of ions in solution. For example, the reaction of the chloride ion (from sodium chloride) may be written.

1. $NaCl(aq) + AgNO_3(aq) \longrightarrow AgCl(s) + NaNO_3(aq)$

2. $Na^+(aq) + Cl^-(aq) + Ag^+(aq) + NO_3^-(aq) \longrightarrow AgCl(s) + Na^+(aq) + NO_3^-(aq)$

3. $Cl^-(aq) + Ag^+(aq) \longrightarrow AgCl(s)$

Equation (1) is the **formula (un-ionized) equation;** it shows the formulas of the substances in the equation as they are normally written. Equation (2) is the **total ionic equation;** it shows the substances as they occur in solution. Strong electrolytes are written as ions; weak electrolytes, precipitates, and gases are written in their un-ionized or molecular form. Equation (3) is the **net ionic equation;** it includes only those substances or ions in Equation (2) that have undergone a chemical change. Thus Na^+ and NO_3^- (sometimes called the "spectator" ions) have not changed and do not appear in the net ionic equation. In both the total ionic and net ionic equations, the atoms and charges must be balanced.

PROCEDURE

Wear protective glasses

1. Clean eight test tubes and rinse each twice with 5 mL of distilled water. The first six test tubes are for the known solutions that will be tested to demonstrate the expected reactions with each anion. Use a marker to label these tubes as follows: NaCl, NaBr, NaI, Na_2SO_4, Na_3PO_4 and Na_2CO_3. The last two tubes are for your unknowns and should be left blank for now. Arrange these test tubes in order in your test tube rack.

2. Clean and rinse two more test tubes and take them to your instructor for your unknown solutions and their identification code. Label them with the code numbers immediately. To avoid possible confusion with the empty unknown test tubes in the rack, put these coded tubes aside in a beaker. Record the code of these unknowns in the top right-hand columns of your report form and label each of the blank tubes in the rack with one of these unknown code numbers.

Pour 2 mL (no more) of each of the six known solutions—one solution per tube—and 2 mL of the corresponding unknown into each unknown tube. Save the remaining portions of the unknown solutions for tests B and C.

You can save considerable time by measuring out 2 mL into the first test tube and using the height of this liquid in the test tube as a guide for measuring out the others.

 Dispose of solutions containing decane in the container marked "Waste organic solvents." Dispose of solutions containing silver, and barium, in the "heavy metals waste" container.

> For each of the following tests that will be performed on known and unknown solutions, there is a corresponding block on the report form where observations should be recorded. If a precipitate forms, record "ppt formed" and include its color. If no precipitate forms, record "no ppt." When dissolving precipitates, record "ppt dissolved" or "ppt did not dissolve." For the decane solubility test, indicate the color of the decane layer.

A. Silver Nitrate Test

 Silver nitrate will stain your skin black. If any silver nitrate gets on your hands, wash it off immediately to avoid these stains.

Add about 1 mL of 0.1 M silver nitrate solution to each test tube. Record the results. Now add about 3 mL of dilute (6 M) nitric acid to each test tube; stopper and shake well. Record the results.

B. Barium Chloride Test

Wash all eight test tubes and rinse each tube twice with distilled water. Again put about 2 mL of the specified solution into each of the eight test tubes. Add about 2 mL of 0.1 M barium chloride solution to each test tube and mix. Record the results. Now add 3 mL of dilute hydrochloric acid to each tube; stopper and shake well. Record the results.

C. Organic Solvent Test

Again wash and rinse all eight test tubes. Again put about 2 mL of the specified solution into each of the eight test tubes. Now add about 2 mL of decane and about 2 mL of chlorine water to each test tube; stopper and shake well. Record the results.

After completing the three tests, compare the results of the known solutions with your observations for your unknown solutions. Record the formula of the anion present in each solution on the report form (Part D).

EXPERIMENT 15

Quantitative Preparation of Potassium Chloride

MATERIALS AND EQUIPMENT

Solid: potassium bicarbonate ($KHCO_3$). **Solution:** 6 M hydrochloric acid (HCl).

DISCUSSION

In this experiment you will examine and verify the mole and mass relationships involved in the quantitative preparation of potassium chloride. Potassium bicarbonate is the source of the potassium ion, and hydrochloric acid is the source of chloride ions. The reaction is expressed in the following equation, which shows that potassium bicarbonate and hydrochloric acid react with each other in a 1-to-1-mole ratio:

$$KHCO_3(aq) + HCl(aq) \longrightarrow KCl(aq) + H_2O(l) + CO_2(g)$$

Furthermore, for every mole of potassium bicarbonate present, 1 mole of potassium chloride is formed. From these molar relationships we can calculate the amount of potassium chloride that is theoretically obtainable from any specified amount of potassium bicarbonate in the reaction. The experimental value can then be compared to the theoretical value.

To conduct the experiment quantitatively, we need to react all the potassium ion from a known amount of potassium bicarbonate and to isolate the KCl in pure a form as feasible. To ensure complete reaction of the potassium bicarbonate, an excess of hydrochloric acid is used The end of the reaction is detectable because the evolution of the gaseous product CO_2 stops when all the $KHCO_3$ has been reacted.

Use the following relationships in your calculations:

1. 1 mole $KHCO_3$ reacted = 1 mole HCl reacted = 1 mole KCl produced

2. 1 mole of solute = 1 molar mass of solute

$$\text{Example:} \quad \text{moles } KHCO_3 = (\text{g } KHCO_3)\left(\frac{1 \text{ mol } KHCO_3}{100.1 \text{ g } KHCO_3}\right)$$

3. Molarity $= \dfrac{\text{moles solute}}{\text{L solution}}$ and for the HCl used in this reaction we can set up the conversion factors

$$\frac{6.0 \text{ mol HCl}}{1 \text{ L}} \quad \text{or} \quad \frac{6.0 \text{ mol HCl}}{1000 \text{ mL}}$$

Note that molarity is an expression of concentration, the units of which are *always* moles of solute per liter of solution from which conversions factors for mol $\longleftrightarrow$ volume can be derived.

For example, if you wanted to determine the volume of 2.0 M HCl that would be used to complete the reaction with 5.5000 g of KHCO$_3$, the dimensional analysis setup would be:

$$\text{mL HCl} = (5.5000\,\text{g KHCO}_3)\left(\frac{1\,\text{mole KHCO}_3}{100.1\,\text{g KHCO}_3}\right)\left(\frac{1\,\text{mol HCl}}{1\,\text{mol KHCO}_3}\right)\left(\frac{1000\,\text{mL}}{2.0\,\text{mol HCl}}\right) = 27\,\text{mL HCl}$$

4. Percentage error $= \left(\dfrac{\text{theoretical value} - \text{experimental value}}{\text{theoretical value}}\right)(100)$

The sequence of major experimental steps in this experiment is as follows:

1. Weigh an evaporating dish.

2. Weigh 2-3 g potassium bicarbonate into the evaporating dish.

3. Dissolve potassium bicarbonate in 5 mL distilled water.

4. Add hydrocholoric acid solution slowly until the fizzing stops.

5. Evaporate the liquid to obtain the dry product, KCl.

6. Heat and dry the KCl to constant weight.

7. Determine the mass of KCl produced.

$$2.50\,\text{g KHCO}_3 \times \frac{1\,\text{mol KHCO}_3}{100.1\,\text{g KHCO}_3} \times \frac{1\,\text{mol KCl}}{1\,\text{mol KHCO}_3} \times \frac{75.55\,\text{g KCl}}{1\,\text{mol KCl}}$$

PROCEDURE

$$= 1.893\,\text{g KCl}.$$

Wear protective glasses.

---

1. Make all weighings *to the highest precision* possible with the balance available.

2. Use the same balance for all weighings.

3. Record all data directly on the report form as they are obtained.

---

1. Weigh a clean, dry evaporating dish.

2. Now add between 2 and 3 g (no more) of potassium bicarbonate to the evaporating dish and reweigh.   *2.50 g*   *KHCO$_3$*

3. Dissolve the potassium bicarbonate in 5 mL of distilled water. If all the potassium bicarbonate does not completely dissolve, do not worry about it. Continue on with the next step.

4. In a graduated cylinder, obtain 6.0 mL of 6 M HCl and **slowly, *with* stirring,** add it to the bicarbonate solution. (The product is formed in this step).

5. Using a beaker of water to make a water bath as shown in Experiment 1, Part C, evaporate the liquid from the solution of potassium chloride. Replenish the water in the water bath as needed. When the water has essentially evaporated (the residue in the dish

looks dry), allow the system to cool for a few minutes; remove the evaporating dish and thoroughly dry the bottom of the dish.

6. The following method of drying the product must be followed to avoid spattering and loss of product. Pay attention during this procedure. Do not leave the drying setup unattended.

   Adjust the burner so you have a nonluminous, 10 to 15 cm (4 to 6 in.) flame **without a distinct inner cone.** Place the evaporating dish on a wire gauze 4-6 in. above the top of the barrel. Heat the dish and contents for 5-10 minutes (the KCl should appear dry). Touch the surface with a stirring rod to prevent the formation of a crust. If spattering occurs remove the burner momentarily and either lower the flame or raise the dish before continuing heating.

7. Cool the dish, weigh, and reheat for an additional 5 minutes. Cool again and reweigh. If the second weighing is within 0.08 g of the first, the KCl may be considered dry. If the second weighing has decreased more than 0.08 g, a third heating (5 minutes) and weighing is necessary. The experiment is complete after obtaining constant weight (within 0.08 g). If constant weight is not obtained after three heatings, your instructor will provide instructions on what to do.

8. From the data collected, determine the mass of KCl produced.

 9. Dissolve the KCl in water and wash it down the sink.

Experiment 17   Reaction Rates, using Spectroscopy (Colorimetry)

Purpose:

Monitor the progress of a chemical reaction by measuring the amount of colored light absorbed by the solution as the reaction progresses. Examine the effects of Temperature on a chemical reaction.

Background Information:

A colorimeter (spectrophotometer) measures the amount of colored light absorbed by or transmitted through a solution. The amount of light, and what color light, is absorbed or transmitted depends on properties of the solution, including the concentration of particles in it. Therefore, when a solution is analyzed with a colorimeter, properties of the solution such as its concentration can be determined.

Grape juice will be mixed with other liquids in this activity to determine if a chemical reaction occurs. Typically, a dark-colored liquid such as grape juice will absorb a greater amount of light energy (i.e., less light will be transmitted through it) than a light-colored liquid with similar properties. If a chemical reaction occurs and changes the color of the solution, it would be reasonable to expect that the solution's ability to absorb light would also change. This method of analysis can be particularly useful when a subtle color change (one that is difficult to observe or quantify with the human eye) occurs as a result of a chemical reaction. Grape juice will be tested with water, household bleach (a dilute aqueous solution of sodium hypochlorite), and a household solution of hydrogen peroxide.

Hypothesize: Will the grape juice react with water, bleach, and/or the hydrogen peroxide? In which case will the reaction proceed fastest? How will the solution's ability to absorb colored light change as a reaction takes place?

Equipment and Supplies:

For each lab group:

Colorimeter, cuvettes (packaged with the Colorimeter Sensor), Grape juice (Welches$_{tm}$), approx. 80 mL , Household bleach, Hydrogen peroxide 3% solution, 50 mL beakers, 25 & 10-mL graduated cylinders , Distilled water Marking pen or labels for beakers, 3 Alka-Seltzer tablets, Stopwatch or clock for time readings

Part I   Rate of Reaction;   Experimental Procedure:

Data Collection & Recording

1. Fill a cuvette with distilled water to the mark. (used for calibration purposes)

2. For the most accurate results, calibrate the Colorimeter using this cuvette containing distilled water. Set the wavelength at **550** nm. Calibrate the colorimeter to an Absorbance of zero

3. Using a graduated cylinder measure out 20 mL of juice and transfer it to a 50 mL beaker add 2 mL of distilled water.to the grape juice. Stir the solution. Proceed to step 4 as quickly as possible!

4. Fill a cuvette to the mark with the above solution. Place the cuvette in the Colorimeter and begin recording absorbance data. Immediately note the initial absorbance value.

5. Continue to record absorbance data for 5 minutes **(Table I)**. Taking readings every minute. Remove the cuvette from the cuvette holder. Note the color of the solution.

6. Repeat steps #2-5 adding 2mL of bleach to 20 mL of fresh juice **(a). (Don't forget to stir in each case. Transfer to a cuvette and begin taking readings as soon as possible)** Note: If 2 mL gives too high or too low an "A" lower or increase the amount of bleach

7. Repeat steps #2-5 adding 8mL of H_2O_2 to 20 mL of fresh juice **(b). (Don't forget to stir in each case. Transfer to a cuvette and begin taking readings as soon as possible).** Note: If 8 mL gives too high or too low an "A" lower or increase the amount of peroxide

Data Analysis:

Graph the data for grape juice and bleach in Figure 1 (F1). Use the y axis for Absorbance and the x axis for time. Be sure to label each axis. Repeat this procedure for the grape juice and hydrogen peroxide using Figure 2 (F2)

Part II   Selection of Optimum Wavelength;   Procedure:

1. This experiment measured absorbance of red light through the test solutions. Fill two cuvettes one with distilled water and one with grape juice. At each of the wavelengths in **Table II** first zero the instrument with the distilled water and then take an Absorbance reading with the grape juice. Attach a graph (Figure 3) (F3) to your laboratory report plotting Absorbance (A) on the y axis and wavelength (λ) on the x axis. Does the maximum Absorbance appear at the wavelength at which you did the experiment?

Part III   Temperature and Reaction Rate;   Procedure:

1.Run water from the hot water tap until it seems as hot as possible. Fill a 250 mL beaker about half full and measure the Temperature of the water. Drop an Alka-Seltzer tablet into the water and using the stopwatch measure the time in seconds it took to completely dissolve. Record your data in **Table III**.

2.Repeat this procedure for water at room temperature (or cold tap water) and for ice water. In each case report your data in **Table III**. Graph your data points (water temperature °K ,on the y axis, versus time, on the x axis) in Figure 4 (F4)

Experiment 17   **Report Sheet**

Name_____   **Partner**_____

Table I   A vs Time

Absorbance	Juice + Water	Juice + Bleach (a)	Juice + Peroxide (b)
0 min			
1 min			
2 min			
3min			
4 min			
5 min			
Color			

Table II   A vs λ

Absorbance (A)						
Wavelength (λ)	520 nm	530 nm	540 nm	550 nm	560 nm	570 nm

Table III

Time, (seconds)			
Temperature, ^{o}C			
Temperature, ^{o}K			

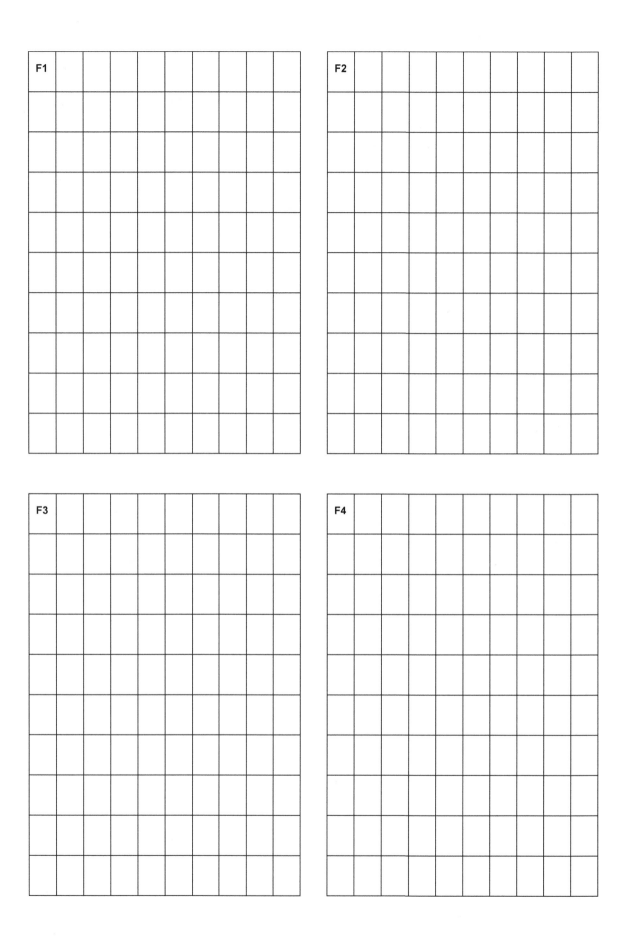

Experiment 17   **Report Sheet**

Name_____

Post Laboratory Questions

1. Does your plot of Absorbance versus wavelength verify the wavelength (550 nm) chosen for the analysis in the setup above? Explain?

1. Did the absorbance of any cuvette increase when compared to the juice plus water solution? Explain.

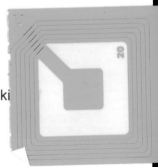

2. In which cuvettes was evidence of a chemical reaction measurable? What ki evidence indicated a reaction occurred?

3. What was the purpose of testing grape juice with distilled water?

EXPERIMENT 19

Charles' Law

MATERIALS AND EQUIPMENT

125 mL Erlenmeyer flask, one-hole rubber stopper, glass and rubber tubing, pneumatic trough, thermometer, screw clamp.

DISCUSSION

The quantitative relationship between the volume and the absolute temperature of a gas is summarized in Charles' law. This law states: at constant pressure, the volume of a particular sample of gas is directly proportional to the absolute temperature.

Charles' law may be expressed mathematically:

$$V \propto T \qquad \text{(constant pressure)} \qquad (1)$$

$$V = kT \quad \text{or} \quad \frac{V}{T} = k \quad \text{(constant pressure)} \qquad (2)$$

where V is volume, T is Kelvin temperature, and k is a proportionality constant dependent on the number of moles and the pressure of the gas.

If the volume of the same sample of gas is measured at two temperatures, $V_1/T_1 = k$ and $V_2/T_2 = k$, and we may say that

$$\frac{V_1}{T_1} = \frac{V_2}{T_2} \quad \text{or} \quad V_2 = (V_1)\left(\frac{T_2}{T_1}\right) \qquad \text{(constant pressure)} \qquad (3)$$

where V_1 and T_1 represent one set of conditions and V_2 and T_2 a different set of conditions, with pressure the same at both conditions.

Experimental Verification of Charles' Law

This experiment measures the volume of an air sample at two temperatures, a high temperature, T_H, and a low temperature, T_L. The volume of the air sample at the high temperature, (V_H), decreases when the sample is cooled to the low temperature and becomes V_L. All of these measurements are made directly. The experimental data is then used to verify Charles' law by two methods:

1. The experimental volume (V_{exp}) measured at the low temperature is compared to the V_L predicted by Charles' law where

$$V_L(theoretical) = (V_H)\left(\frac{T_L}{T_H}\right)$$

2. The V/T ratios for the air sample measured at both the high and the low temperatures are compared. Charles' law predicts that these ratios will be equal.

$$\frac{V_H}{T_H} = \frac{V_L}{T_L}$$

Pressure Considerations

The relationship between temperature and volume defined by Charles' law is valid only if the pressure is the same when the volume is measured at each temperature. That is not the case in this experiment.

1. The volume, V_H, of air at the higher temperature, T_H, is measured at atmospheric pressure, P_{atm} in a dry Erlenmeyer flask. The air is assumed to be dry and the pressure is obtained from a barometer.

2. The experimental air volume, (V_{exp}) at the lower temperature, T_L, is measured over water. This volume is saturated with water vapor that contributes to the total pressure in the flask. Therefore, the experimental volume must be corrected to the volume of dry air at atmospheric pressure. This is done using Boyle's law as follows:

   a. The partial pressure of the dry air, P_{DA}, is calculated by subtracting the vapor pressure of water from atmospheric pressure:

   $$P_{DA} = P_{atm} - P_{H_2O}$$

   b. The volume that this dry air would occupy at P_{atm} is then calculated using the Boyle's law equation:

   $$(V_{DA})(P_{atm}) = (V_{exp})(P_{DA})$$
   $$(V_{DA}) = \frac{(V_{exp})(P_{DA})}{(P_{atm})}$$

PROCEDURE

Wear protective glasses.

 No waste for disposal in this experiment.

> **NOTE:** It is essential that the Erlenmeyer flask and rubber stopper assembly be as dry as possible in order to obtain reproducible results.

Dry a 125 mL Erlenmeyer flask by gently heating the entire outer surface with a burner flame. Care must be used in heating to avoid breaking the flask. If the flask is wet, first wipe the inner and outer surfaces with a towel to remove nearly all the water. Then, holding the flask with a test tube holder, gently heat the entire flask. Avoid placing the flask directly in the flame. Allow to cool.

While the flask is cooling select a 1-hole rubber stopper to fit the flask and insert a 5 cm piece of glass tubing into the stopper so that the end of the tubing is flush with the bottom of the stopper. Attach a 3 cm piece of rubber tubing to the glass tubing (see Figure 19.1). Insert the stopper into the flask and mark (wax pencil) the distance that it is inserted. Clamp the flask so that it is submerged as far as possible in water contained in a 400 mL beaker (without the flask touching the bottom of the beaker) (see Figure 19.2).

Heat the water to boiling. Keep the flask in the gently boiling water for at least 8 minutes to allow the air in the flask to attain the temperature of the boiling water. Add water as needed to maintain the water level in the beaker. Read and record the temperature of the boiling water.

While the flask is still in the boiling water, seal it by clamping the rubber tubing tightly with a screw clamp. Remove the flask from the hot water and submerge it in a pan of cold water, keeping the top down at all times to avoid losing air (see Figure 19.3). Remove the screw clamp, letting the cold water flow into the flask. Keep the flask totally submerged for about 6 minutes to allow the flask and contents to attain the temperature of the water. Read and record the temperature of the water in the pan.

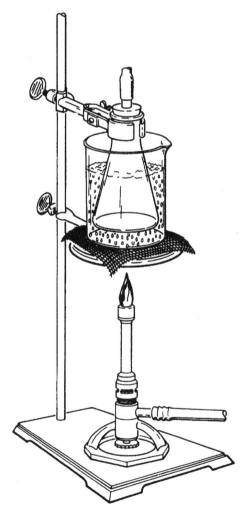

Figure 19.1   Rubber stopper assembly

Figure 19.2   Heating the flask (and air) in boiling water

In order to equalize the pressure inside the flask with that of the atmosphere, bring the water level in the flask to the same level as the water in the pan by raising or lowering the flask (see Figure 19.3). With the water levels equal, pinch the rubber tubing to close the flask. Remove the flask from the water and set it down on the laboratory bench.

Using a graduated cylinder carefully measure and record the volume of water in the flask.

Repeat the entire experiment. Use the same flask and flame dry again; **make sure that the rubber stopper assembly is thoroughly dried inside and outside.**

After the second trial fill the flask to the brim with water and insert the stopper assembly to the mark, letting the glass and rubber fill to the top and overflow. Measure the volume of water in the flask. Since this volume is the total volume of the flask, record it as the volume of air at the higher temperature. Because the same flask is used in both trials, it is necessary to make this measurement only once.

Figure 19.3   Equalizing the pressure in the flask. The water level inside the flask is adjusted to the level of the water in the pan by raising or lowering the flask

REPORT FOR EXPERIMENT 19

Charles' Law

$$\frac{V_1}{T_1} = \frac{V_2}{T_2} \quad (\text{temp.} \downarrow, \text{ volume} \downarrow)$$

Data Table

	Trial 1	Trial 2
Temperature of boiling water, T_H	100 °C, 373 K	94 °C, 367 K
Temperature of cold water, T_L	20 °C, 293 K	2 °C, 275 K
Volume of water collected in flask (decrease in the volume of air due to cooling)	40.0 mL	57.0 mL
Volume of air at higher temperature, V_H (volume of flask measured only after Trial 2)	130.0 mL	253 mL
Volume of wet air at lower temperature (volume of flask less volume of water collected), V_{exp}	130.0 mL − 40.0 mL = 90.0 mL	196 mL
Atmosphere pressure, P_{atm} (barometer reading)	760 mm Hg	754.3 mmHg
Vapor pressure of water at lower temperature, P_{H_2O} (see Appendix 6)	17.5 mmHg	4.6 mmHg

REPORT FOR EXPERIMENT 19 (continued)   NAME Tran Nguyen

CALCULATIONS: In the spaces below, show calculation setups for Trial 1 only. Show answers for both trials in the boxes

	Trial 1	Trial 2
1. (a)		$754.3 - 4.6$
	$742.5 \, mmHg$	$= 749.7 \, mmHg$
1. (b)	$87.9 \, mL$	$(196.)\left(\dfrac{749.7}{754.3}\right)$
		$= 195 \, mL$
2.	$102 \, mL$	$(253)\left(\dfrac{275}{367}\right)$
		$= 190 \, mL$
3.	$13.8 \, \%$	$\left(\dfrac{190 - 195}{190}\right) \times 100$
		$-2.63 \, \%$
4. (a)	0.349	$\dfrac{253 \, mL}{367 \, K} = .689$
4. (b)	0.300	$\dfrac{195 \, mL}{275 \, K} = .709$

1. Corrected experimental volume of dry air at the lower temperature calculated from data obtained at the lower temperature.

   (a) Pressure of dry air (P_{DA})

   $P_{DA} = P_{Atm} - P_{H_2O}$

   $760 - 17.5 = 742.5$

   (b) Corrected experimental volume of dry air (lower temperature).

   $V_{DA} = (V_{exp})\left(\dfrac{P_{DA}}{P_{Atm}}\right) =$

   $(90.0 \, mL)\left(\dfrac{742.5 \, mmHg}{760 \, mmHg}\right)$

2. Predicted volume of dry air at lower temperature V_L calculated by Charles' law from volume at higher temperature (V_H). ✶ used K

   $V_L = (V_H)\left(\dfrac{T_L}{T_H}\right)$

   $(130.0 \, mL)\left(\dfrac{293 \, K}{373 \, K}\right)$

3. Percentage error in verification of Charles' law.

   $\% \, error = \left(\dfrac{V_L - V_{DA}}{V_L}\right)(100) =$

   $\dfrac{102 \, mL - 87.9 \, mL}{102 \, mL} (100)$

4. Comparison of experimental V/T ratios. (Use dry volumes and absolute temperatures.)

   (a) $\dfrac{V_H}{T_H} = \dfrac{130.0 \, mL}{373 \, K} = 0.349$

   (b) $\dfrac{V_{DA}}{T_L} = \dfrac{87.9 \, mL}{293 \, K} = 0.300$

139

REPORT FOR EXPERIMENT 19 (continued)   NAME _Tran Nguyen_

5. On the graph paper provided, plot the volume-temperature values used in Calculation 4. Temperature data **must be in °C.** Draw a straight line between the two plotted points and extrapolate (extend) the line so that it crosses the temperature axis.

QUESTIONS AND PROBLEMS

1. (a) In the experiment, why are the water levels inside and outside the flask equalized before removing the flask from the cold water?

   because to equilize the pressure inside the flask w/ that of the atmosphere

   (b) When the water level is higher inside than outside the flask, is the gas pressure in the flask higher than, lower than, or the same as, the atmospheric pressure? (specify which)

   lower than

2. A 125 mL sample of dry air at 230°C is cooled to 100°C at constant pressure. What volume will the dry air occupy at 100°C?

   $V_1 = 125$ mL

   $T_1 = 230°C = 503$ K

   $T_2 = 100°C = 373$ K

   $\dfrac{V_1}{T_1} = \dfrac{V_2}{T_2}$

   $V_2 = \dfrac{V_1 \cdot T_2}{T_1} = \dfrac{125 \times 373}{503}$

   _92.7_ mL

3. A 250 mL container of a gas is at 150°C. At what temperature will the gas occupy a volume of 125 mL, the pressure remaining constant?

   $V_1 = 250$ mL

   $T_1 = 150°C = 423$ K

   $V_2 = 125$ mL

   $T_2 = \dfrac{T_1 \cdot V_2}{V_1}$

   $= \dfrac{423 \times 125}{250} = 211.5$ K

   _-61.65_ °C

4. (a) An open flask of air is cooled. Answer the following:

   1. Under which conditions, before or after cooling, does the flask contain more gas molecules?

   after

   2. Is the pressure in the flask at the lower temperature the same as, greater than, or less than the pressure in the flask before it was cooled?

   greater than

(b) An open flask of air is heated, stoppered in the heated condition, and then allowed to cool back to room temperature. Answer the following:

1. Does the flask contain the same, more, or fewer gas molecules now compared to before it was heated?

   _____fewer_____

2. Is the volume occupied by the gas in the flask approximately the same, greater, or less than before it was heated?

   _____same_____

3. Is the pressure in the flask the same, greater, or less than before the flask was heated?

   _____less than_____

4. Do any of the above conditions explain why water rushed into the flask at the lower temperature in the experiment? Amplify your answer.

   Yes. #3 shows that the pressure in the flask is less than before the flask was heated. So, water will rushed into the flask at the lower temp. that is from outside to inside the flask ...

5. On the graph you plotted,

   (a) At what temperature does the extrapolated line intersect the x-axis?

   _____−140_____ °C

   (b) At what temperature does Charles' law predict that the extrapolated line should intersect the x-axis?

   _____−300_____ °C

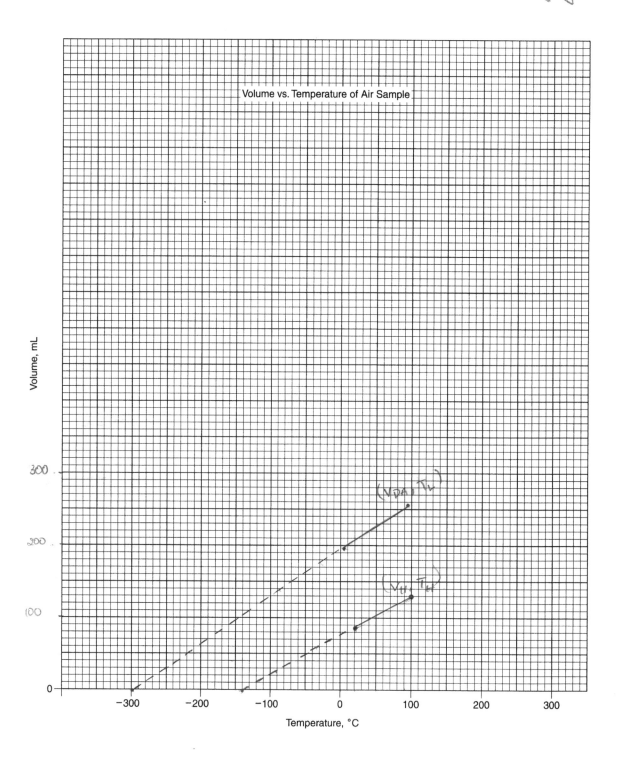

Volume vs. Temperature of Air Sample

Volume, mL

Temperature, °C

(V_{DA}, T_{H})

(V_{H}, T_{H})

300

200

100

0

−300   −200   −100   0   100   200   300

EXPERIMENT 22

Neutralization–Titration I

MATERIALS AND EQUIPMENT

Solid: potassium hydrogen phthalate, abbreviated KHP ($KHC_8H_4O_4$). **Liquids:** phenolphthalein indicator, unknown base solution (NaOH). One buret (25 mL or 50 mL) and buret clamp, buret brush. Wash bottle for distilled water.

DISCUSSION

The reaction of an acid and a base to form a salt and water is known as **neutralization.** In this experiment potassium hydrogen phthalate (abbreviated KHP) is used as the acid. Potassium hydrogen phthalate is an organic substance having the formula $HKC_8H_4O_4$, and like HCl, has only one acid hydrogen atom per molecule. Because of its complex formula, potassium hydrogen phthalate is commonly called KHP Despite its complex formula we see that the reaction of KHP with sodium hydroxide is similar to that of HCl. One mole of KHP reacts with one mole of NaOH.

$$HKC_8H_4O_4 + NaOH \longrightarrow NaKC_8H_4O_4 + H_2O$$

$$HCl + NaOH \longrightarrow NaCl + H_2O$$

Titration is the process of measuring the volume of one reagent required to react with a measured volume or mass of another reagent. In this experiment we will determine the molarity of a base (NaOH) solution from data obtained by titrating KHP with the base solution. The base solution is added from a buret to a flask containing a weighed sample of KHP dissolved in water. From the mass of KHP used we calculate the moles of KHP. Exactly the same number of moles of base is needed to neutralize this number of moles of KHP since one mole of NaOH reacts with one mole of KHP. We then calculate the molarity of the base solution from the titration volume and the number of moles of NaOH in that volume.

In the titration, the point of neutralization, called the **end-point,** is observed when an indicator, placed in the solution being titrated, changes color. The indicator selected is one that changes color when the stoichiometric quantity of base (according to the chemical equation) has been added to the acid. A solution of phenolphthalein, an organic acid, is used as the indicator in this experiment. Phenolphthalein is colorless in acid solution but changes to pink when the solution becomes slightly alkaline. When the number of moles of sodium hydroxide added is equal to the number of moles of KHP originally present, the reaction is complete. The next drop of sodium hydroxide added changes the indicator from colorless to pink.

Use the following relationships in your calculations:

1. According to the equation for the reaction,

   Moles of KHP reacted = Moles of NaOH reacted

2. $Moles = \dfrac{g \text{ of solute}}{molar \text{ mass of solute}}$

3. Molarity is an expression of concentration, the units of which are moles of solute per liter of solution:

$$\text{Molarity} = \frac{\text{moles}}{\text{liter}}$$

Thus, a 1.00 molar (1.00 M) solution contains 1.00 mole of solute in 1 liter of solution. A 0.100 M solution, then, contains 0.100 mole of solute in 1 liter of solution.

4. The number of moles of solute present in a known volume of solution of known concentration can be calculated by multiplying the volume of the solution (in liters) by the molarity of the solution:

$$\text{Moles} = (\text{liters})(\text{molarity}) = (\text{liters})\left(\frac{\text{moles}}{\text{liter}}\right)$$

PROCEDURE

Wear protective glasses.

 Dispose of all solutions in the sink.

Make all weighings to the highest precision of the balance.

Obtain some solid KHP in a test tube or vial. Weigh two samples of KHP into 125 mL Erlenmeyer flasks, numbered for identification. (The flasks should be rinsed with distilled water, but need not be dry on the inside.) First weigh the flask, then add KHP to the flask by tapping the test tube or vial until 1.000 to 1.200 g has been added (see Figure 22.1). Determine the mass of the flask and the KHP. In a similar manner weigh another sample of KHP into the second flask. To each flask add approximately 30 mL of distilled water. If some KHP is sticking to the walls of the flask, rinse it down with water from a wash bottle. Warm the flasks slightly and swirl them until all the KHP is dissolved.

Figure 22.1   Method of adding KHP from a vial to a weighed Erlenmeyer flask

Obtain one buret and clean it. See "Use of the Buret," on the following page for instructions on cleaning and using the buret. Read and record all buret volumes to the nearest 0.01 mL.

Obtain about 250 mL of a base (NaOH) of unknown molarity in a clean, **dry** 250 mL Erlenmeyer flask as directed by your instructor. Record the number of this unknown.

1. Keep your base solution stoppered when not in use.

2. The 250 mL sample of base is intended to be used in both this experiment and Experiment 23. Be sure to label and save it.

Rinse the buret with two 5 to 10 mL portions of the base, running the second rinsing through the buret tip. Discard the rinsings in the sink. Fill the buret with the base, making sure that the tip is completely filled and contains no air bubbles. Adjust the level of the liquid in the buret so that the bottom of the meniscus is at exactly 0.00 mL. Record the initial buret reading (0.00 mL) in the space provided on the report form.

Add 3 drops of phenolphthalein solution to each 125 mL flask containing KHP and water. Place the first (Sample 1) on a piece of white paper under the buret extending the tip of the buret into the flask (see Figure 22.2).

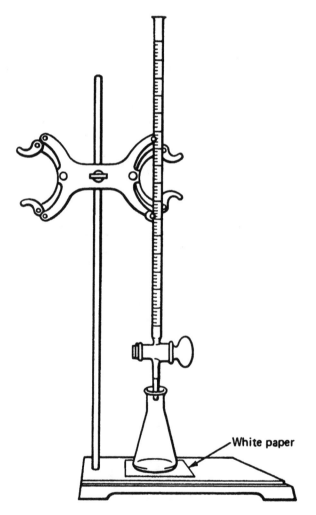

Figure 22.2 Setup with stopcock buret

Titrate the KHP by adding base until the end-point is reached. The titration is conducted by swirling the solution in the flask with the right hand (if you are right handed) while manipulating the stopcock with the left (Figure 22.3). As base is added you will observe a pink color caused by localized high base concentration. Toward the end-point the color flashes throughout the solution, remaining for a longer time. When this occurs, add the base drop by drop until the end-point is reached, as indicated by the first drop of base which causes a faint pink color to remain in the entire solution for at least 30 seconds. Read and record the final buret reading (see Figure 22.5). Refill the buret to the zero mark and repeat the titration with Sample 2. Then, calculate the molarity of the base in each sample. If these molarities differ by more than 0.004, titrate a third sample.

When you are finished with the titrations, empty and rinse the buret at least twice (including the tip) with tap water and once with distilled water. Return the vial with the unused KHP.

Use of the Buret

A buret is a volumetric instrument that is calibrated to deliver a measured volume of solution. The 50 mL buret is calibrated from 0 to 50 mL in 0.1 mL increments and is read to the nearest 0.01 mL. All volumes delivered from the buret should be between the calibration marks. (Do not estimate above the 0 mL mark or below the 50 mL mark.)

1. **Cleaning the Buret.** The buret must be clean in order to deliver the calibrated volume. Drops of liquid clinging to the sides as the buret is drained are evidence of a dirty buret.

To clean the buret, first rinse it a couple of times with tap water, pouring the water from a beaker. Then scrub it with a detergent solution, using a long-handled buret brush. Rinse the buret several times with tap water and finally with distilled water. Check for cleanliness by draining the distilled water through the tip and observe whether droplets of water remain on the inner walls of the buret.

2. **Using the Buret.** After draining the distilled water, rinse the buret with two 5 to 10 mL portions of the titrating solution to be used in it. This rinsing is done by holding the buret in a horizontal position and rolling the solution around to wet the entire inner surface. Allow the final rinsing to drain through the tip.

Fill the buret with the solution to slightly above the 0 mL mark and adjust it to 0.00 mL, or some other volume below this mark, by draining the solution through the tip. The buret tip must be completely filled to deliver the volume measured.

To deliver the solution from the buret, turn the stopcock with the forefinger and the thumb of your left hand (if you are right handed) to allow the solution to enter the flask. (See Figure 22.3). This procedure leaves your right hand free to swirl the solution in the flask during the titration. With a little practice you can control the flow so that increments as small as 1 drop of solution can be delivered.

3. **Reading the Buret.** The smallest calibration mark of a 50 mL buret is 0.1 mL. However, the buret is read to the nearest 0.01 mL by estimating between the calibration marks. When reading the buret be sure your line of sight is level with the bottom of the meniscus in order to avoid parallax errors (see Figure 22.4). The exact bottom of the meniscus may be made more prominent and easier to read by allowing the meniscus to pick up the reflection from a heavy dark line on a piece of paper (see Figure 22.5).

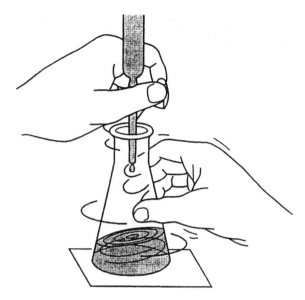

Figure 22.3   Titration technique

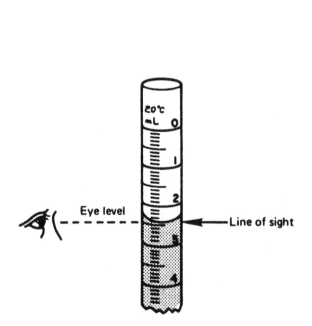

Figure 22.4   Reading the buret. The line of sight must be level with the bottom of the meniscus to avoid parallax.

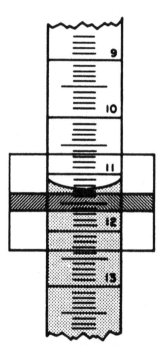

Figure 22.5   Reading the meniscus. A heavy dark line brought to within one division of the meniscus will make the meniscus more prominent and easier to read. The volume reading is 11.28 mL.

REPORT FOR EXPERIMENT 22

Neutralization – Titration I

Data Table

	Sample 1	Sample 2	Sample 3 (if needed)
Mass of flask and KHP			
Mass of empty flask			
Mass of KHP			
Final buret reading			
Initial buret reading			
Volume of base used			

CALCULATIONS: In the spaces below show calculation setups **for Sample 1 only.** Show answers for both samples in the boxes. Remember to use the proper number of significant figures in all calculations. (The number 0.005 has only one significant figure.)

	Sample 1	Sample 2	Sample 3 (if needed)
1. Moles of acid (KHP, Molar mass = 204.2)			
2. Moles of base used to neutralize (react with) the above number of moles of acid			
3. Molarity of base (NaOH)			

4. Average molarity of base   _____

5. Unknown base number   _____

QUESTIONS AND PROBLEMS

1. If you had added 50 mL of water to a sample of KHP instead of 30 mL, would the titration of that sample then have required more, less, or the same amount of base? Explain.

2. A student weighed out 1.106 g of KHP How many moles was that?

_____ mol

3. A titration required 18.38 mL of 0.1574 M NaOH solution. How many moles of NaOH were in this volume?

_____ mol

4. A student weighed a sample of KHP and found it weighed 1.276 g. Titration of this KHP required 19.84 mL of base (NaOH). Calculate the molarity of the base.

_____ M

5. Forgetful Freddy weighed his KHP sample, but forgot to bring his report sheet along, so he recorded the mass of KHP on a paper towel. During his titration, which required 18.46 mL of base, he spilled some base on his hands. He remembered to wash his hands, but forgot about the data on the towel, and used it to dry his hands. When he went to calculate the molarity of his base, Freddy discovered that he didn't have the mass of his KHP. His kindhearted instructor told Freddy that his base was 0.2987 M. Calculate the mass of Freddy's KHP sample.

_____ g

6. What mass of solid NaOH would be needed to make 645 mL of Freddy's NaOH solution?

_____ g

EXPERIMENT 24

Chemical Equilibrium – Reversible Reactions

MATERIALS AND EQUIPMENT

Solid: ammonium chloride (NH_4Cl). **Solutions:** saturated ammonium chloride, 0.1 M cobalt(II) chloride ($CoCl_2$), 0.1 M iron(III) chloride ($FeCl_3$), concentrated (12 M) hydrochloric acid (HCl), 0.1 M copper(II) sulfate ($CuSO_4$), 6 M ammonium hydroxide (NH_4OH), phenolphthalein, 0.1 M potassium thiocyanate (KSCN), 0.1 M silver nitrate ($AgNO_3$), saturated sodium chloride (NaCl), and dilute (3 M) sulfuric acid (H_2SO_4).

DISCUSSION

In many chemical reactions the reactants are not totally converted to the products because of a reverse reaction; that is, because the products react to form the original reactants. Such reactions are said to be reversible and are indicated by a double arrow ($\rightleftharpoons$) in the equation. The reaction proceeding to the right is called the **forward reaction;** that to the left, the **reverse reaction.** Both reactions occur simultaneously.

Every chemical reaction proceeds at a certain rate or speed. The rate of a reaction is variable and depends on the concentrations of the reactants and the conditions under which the reaction is conducted. When the rate of the forward reaction is equal to the rate of the reverse reaction, a condition of **chemical equilibrium** exists. At equilibrium the products react at the same rate as they are produced. Thus the concentrations of substances in equilibrium do not change, but both reactions, forward and reverse, are still occurring.

The principle of Le Chatelier relates to systems in equilibrium and states that when the conditions of a system in equilibrium are changed the system reacts to counteract the change and reestablish equilibrium. In this experiment we will observe the effect of changing the concentration of one or more substances in a chemical equilibrium. Consider the hypothetical equilibrium system

$$A + B \rightleftharpoons C + D$$

When the concentration of any one of the species in this equilibrium is changed, the equilibrium is disturbed. Changes in the concentrations of all the other substances will occur to establish a new position of equilibrium. For example, when the concentration of B is increased, the rate of the forward reaction increases, the concentration of A decreases, and the concentrations of C and D increase. After a period of time the two rates will become equal and the system will again be in equilibrium. The following statements indicate how the equilibrium will shift when the concentrations of A, B, C, and D are changed.

An increase in the concentration of A or B causes the equilibrium to shift to the right.

An increase in the concentration of C or D causes the equilibrium to shift to the left.

A decrease in the concentration of A or B causes the equilibrium to shift to the left.

A decrease in the concentration of C or D causes the equilibrium to shift to the right.

Evidence of a shift in equilibrium by a change in concentration can easily be observed if one of the substances involved in the equilibrium is colored. The appearance of a precipitate or the change in color of an indicator can sometimes be used to detect a shift in equilibrium.

Net ionic equations for the equilibrium systems to be studied are given below. These equations will be useful for answering the questions in the report form.

A. Saturated Sodium Chloride Solution

$$NaCl(s) \underset{}{\overset{H_2O}{\rightleftharpoons}} Na^+(aq) + Cl^-(aq)$$

B. Saturated Ammonium Chloride Solution

$$NH_4Cl(s) \overset{H_2O}{\rightleftharpoons} NH_4^+(aq) + Cl^-(aq)$$

C. Iron(III) Chloride plus Potassium Thiocyanate

$$Fe^{3+}(aq) + SCN^-(aq) \rightleftharpoons Fe(SCN)^{2+}(aq)$$

Pale   Colorless   Red
yellow

D. Copper(II) Sulfate Solution with Ammonia

$$Cu(H_2O)_4^{2+}(aq) + 4\,NH_3(aq) \rightleftharpoons Cu(OH)_2(s) \rightleftharpoons [Cu(NH_3)_4]^{2+}(aq) + 4\,H_2O$$

light blue   blue   deep blue/purple
clear   cloudy   cloudy

E. Cobalt(II) Chloride Solution

The equilibrium involves the following ions in solutions:

$$Co(H_2O)_6^{2+}(aq) + 4\,Cl^-(aq) \rightleftharpoons CoCl_4^{2-}(aq) + 6\,H_2O(l)$$

Pink   Blue

F. Ammonia Solution

$$NH_3(aq) + H_2O(l) \rightleftharpoons NH_4^+(aq) + OH^-(aq)$$

PROCEDURE

Wear protective glasses.

NOTE: Record observed evidence of equilibrium shifts as each experiment is done.

A. Saturated Sodium Chloride Solution

Add a few drops of conc. hydrochloric acid to 2 to 3 mL of saturated sodium chloride solution in a test tube, and note the results. *appeared white solid at the bottom.*

B. Saturated Ammonium Chloride Solution

Repeat Part A, using saturated ammonium chloride solution instead of sodium chloride solution.

 Dispose of the solutions in A and B in the sink and flush with water.

C. Iron(III) Chloride plus Potassium Thiocyanate

Prepare a stock solution to be tested by adding 2 mL each of 0.1 M iron(III) chloride and 0.1 M potassium thiocyanate solutions to 100 mL of distilled water and mix. Pour about 5 mL of this stock solution into each of four test tubes.

1. Use the first tube as a control for color comparison.

2. Add about 1 mL of 0.1 M iron(III) chloride solution to the second tube and observe the color change.

3. Add about 1 mL of 0.1 M potassium thiocyanate solution to the third tube and observe the color change.

4. Add 0.1 M silver nitrate solution dropwise (less than 1 mL) to the fourth tube until almost all the color is discharged. The white precipitate formed consists of both AgCl and AgSCN. Pour about half the contents (including the precipitate) into another tube. Add 0.1 M potassium thiocyanate solution dropwise (1 to 2 mL) to one tube and 0.1 M iron(III) chloride solution (1 to 2 mL) to the other. Observe the results.

 Dispose of the contents in tubes C.1–3 and the unused stock solutions in the sink and flush with water. Dispose of the contents of both C.4 tubes in the "heavy metals" waste container.

D. Copper (II) Sulfate Solution with Ammonia

Pour 2 mL of 0.1 M copper (II) sulfate into each of two test tubes. Add 6 M $NH_3(aq)$ (NH_4OH) dropwise (shake well after each drop is added) to one of the copper(II) sulfate tubes. When there is a definite color or appearance change, note the change on the report form. Use the second test tube for comparison. Continue to add the $NH_3(aq)$ until there is another color or appearance change. Note the changes on the report form.

Now, add 3 M H_2SO_4 dropwise to the solution until the original color is restored. Again, use the second tube for comparison.

 Dispose of the contents of both test tubes in the "heavy metals" waste container provided.

EXPERIMENT 28

Hydrocarbons

MATERIALS AND EQUIPMENT

Solids: calcium carbide (about 3/8 in. lumps) (CaC_2). **Liquids:** pentene (amylene) (C_5H_{10}), heptane (C_7H_{16}), kerosene, and toluene ($C_6H_5CH_3$). **Solutions:** 5% bromine (Br_2) in 1,1,1-trichloroethane (CCl_3CH_3) and 0.1 M potassium permanganate ($KMnO_4$). Wooden splints.

Hydrocarbons

Hydrocarbons are organic compounds made up entirely of carbon and hydrogen atoms. Their principal natural sources are coal, petroleum, and natural gas. Hydrocarbons are grouped into several series by similarity of molecular structure. Some of these are the alkanes, alkenes, alkynes, and aromatic hydrocarbons.

Alkanes

Also known as the paraffins or **saturated hydrocarbons,** the **alkanes** are straight- or branched-chain hydrocarbons having only single bonds between carbon atoms. They are called saturated hydrocarbons because all their carbon-carbon bonds are single bonds.

The general formula for alkanes is C_nH_{2n+2}

The first 10 members of the alkane series and their molecular formulas are listed below:

Methane CH_4	Hexane C_6H_{14}
Ethane C_2H_6	Heptane C_7H_{16}
Propane C_3H_8	Octane C_8H_{18}
Butane C_4H_{10}	Nonane C_9H_{20}
Pentane C_5H_{12}	Decane $C_{10}H_{22}$

Like most organic substances, the alkanes are combustible. The products of their complete combustion are carbon dioxide and water. The reactions of the alkanes are of the substitution type; that is, some atom or group of atoms is substituted for one or more of the hydrogen atoms in the hydrocarbon molecule. For example, in the bromination of methane, a bromine atom is substituted for a hydrogen atom. This reaction does not occur appreciably in the dark at room temperature but is catalyzed by ultraviolet light. The equation is

$$CH_4 + Br_2 \xrightarrow[\text{light}]{\text{Ultraviolet}} CH_3Br + HBr$$

Methane   Methyl bromide
(Bromethane)

Alkenes

Also known as the olefins, the alkenes are a series of straight- or branched-chain hydrocarbons containing a carbon-carbon double bond in their structures. They are considered to be unsaturated hydrocarbons The first two members of the series are ethene (C_2H_4) and propene (C_3H_6). The general formula for alkenes is C_nH_{2n}. Their structural and condensed structural formulas are:

Ethene (ethylene)   Propene (propylne)

The functional group of this series is the carbon-carbon double bond ($C=C$); it is a point of high reactivity. Alkenes undergo addition-type reactions; that is, other groups are added to the double bond, causing the molecule to become saturated. For example, when hydrogen is added, one H atom from H_2 is added to each carbon atom of the double bond to saturate the molecule, forming an alkane:

$$CH_3CH=CH_2 \;+\; H_2 \xrightarrow[\text{Heat and Pressure}]{\text{Ni Catalyst}} CH_3CH_2CH_3$$

Propene   Propane

When a halogen such as bromine is added, one Br atom from Br_2 is added to each carbon atom of the double bond to saturate the molecule:

$$CH_2=CH_2 \;+\; Br_2 \longrightarrow \underset{\substack{| \quad | \\ Br \quad Br}}{CH_2CH_2}$$

1,2-Dibromoethane
(Ethylene dibromide)

Evidence that bromine has reacted is the disappearance of the red-brown color of free bromine. Other reactions of olefins also show the increased reactivity of the alkenes over the alkanes.

Unsaturated hydrocarbons can be oxidized by potassium permanganate. The reaction is known as the **Baeyer test for unsaturation.** Evidence that reaction has occurred is the rapid disappearance (within a few seconds) of the purple color of the permanganate ion. The resulting reaction products will not be colorless. Potassium permanganate is a very strong oxidizing agent and gives similar results when reacted with other oxidizable substances, such as alcohols.

Alkynes

Also called the **acetylenes,** the alkynes are another class of **unsaturated hydrocarbons,** but they contain a carbon-carbon triple bond in their structures. The first two members of this series are acetylene (ethyne) and propyne:

$$H-C\equiv C-H \qquad\qquad CH_3C\equiv CH$$

Ethyne (Acetylene)   Propyne

Acetylene is the most important member of this series and can be prepared from calcium carbide and water. The equation for this reaction is

$$CaC_2(s) + 2H_2O(l) \longrightarrow CH{\equiv}CH(g) + Ca(OH)_2(aq)$$

Mixtures of acetylene and air are explosive. The alkynes undergo addition-type reactions similar to those of the alkenes.

Aromatic Hydrocarbons

The parent substance of this class of hydrocarbons is benzene (C_6H_6). From its formula benzene appears to be a highly unsaturated molecule; the corresponding six-carbon alkane contains 14 hydrogen atoms per molecule (C_6H_{14}). However, the chemical reactions of benzene show that its behavior is like that of the saturated hydrocarbons in many respects. Its reactions are primarily of the substitution type. In the past, benzene was used extensively in student laboratories to illustrate the properties of aromatic hydrocarbons. Within the last decade, studies have shown benzene to be a cancer-causing substance and it is being eliminated from many experiments. We will use toluene in this experiment instead of benzene.

The carbon atoms in a benzene molecule are arranged in a six-membered ring structure, with one hydrogen atom bonded to each carbon atom. The following diagrams represent the benzene molecule; in the second and third structures it is understood that a carbon and a hydrogen atom are present at each corner of the hexagon or benzene ring.

Benzene
C_6H_6

Toluene
$C_6H_5CH_3$

PROCEDURE

 Wear protective glasses.

In the following reactions, heptane will be used to represent the saturated hydrocarbons; pentene (amylene), the unsaturated hydrocarbons; and toluene, the aromatic hydrocarbons. (Toluene is *only* reacted with potassium permanganate and *not* bromine.)

Note: As you can see from its structure, toluene is not only aromatic but also contains a methyl substituent group. As seen above, bromine reacts with alkanes in the presence of ultraviolet light to produce a substitution derivative. The overhead lighting found in most laboratories supplies sufficient levels of ultraviolet light to cause a bromine substitution reaction to occur slowly with alkanes. Thus, with toluene, bromine does not react at the aromatic ring, but does react, slowly, at the methyl substituent group. Hence, the lack of reactivity between aromatic benzene and bromine can not be effectively demonstrated by mixing aromatic toluene and bromine (the methyl substitution reaction does slowly occur). Further, the product formed, in the presence of ultraviolet light, between bromine and toluene is a mild lachrymator (a tear-producing compound similar to those found in onions) and may be bothersome to some students or very irritating to more susceptible students.

Hydrocarbons are extremely flammable and should not be handled near open flames. Avoid inhaling the vapors, contact with skin and clothing, and do not ingest.

 Dispose of all waste and reaction products in the "organic solvent" waste container provided.

A. Combustion

Obtain about 1 mL (no more) of heptane in an evaporating dish and start it burning by carefully bringing a lighted match or splint to it. Repeat with an equally small volume of pentene. Note the characteristics of the flames.

B. Reaction with Bromine

 CAUTION: Dispense bromine solution under the hood, and be especially careful not to spill bromine on your hands.

Take two clean dry test tubes. Place about 1 mL of heptane in the first tube and 1 mL of pentene in the second. Add 3 drops of 5 percent bromine in trichloroethane solution to each sample; stopper the tubes and note the results. Any tube that still shows bromine color after 1 minute should be exposed to sunlight or to a strong electric light for an additional 2 minutes.

C. Reaction with Potassium Permanganate

The Baeyer test for unsaturation in hydrocarbons involves the reaction of hydrocarbons with potassium permanganate solution. Evidence that reaction has occurred is the rapid disappearance (within a few seconds) of the purple color of the permanganate ion. Potassium permanganate is a very strong oxidizing agent and gives similar results when reacted with other oxidizable substances, such as alcohols.

Add 2 drops of potassium permanganate solution to about 1 mL each of heptane, pentene, and toluene in test tubes. Mix and note the results.

D. Kerosene

Determine which class of hydrocarbons (alkanes, alkenes, or aromatic) kerosene belongs to by reacting it with bromine and with potassium permanganate, as in Tests B and C.

E. Acetylene

In this part of the experiment you will prepare acetylene and test its combustibility.

Fill a 400 mL beaker nearly full of tap water. Fill three test tubes (18 × 150 mm) with water as follows: Tube (1) completely full; Tube (2) 15 mL; and Tube (3) 6 mL.

Obtain a small lump of calcium carbide from the reagent bottle and drop it into the beaker of water. (See Figure 28.1.) Place your thumb over the full test tube of water (Tube 1) and invert it in the beaker. Hold the tube over the bubbling acetylene and, when it is full of gas, stopper it while the tube is still under the water. Displace the water in the other two tubes in the same manner; **stopper them immediately after the water is displaced.**

Test the contents of each tube as follows:

Tube 1. Bring the mouth of the tube to the burner flame as you remove the stopper. After the acetylene ignites, tilt the mouth of the tube up and down.

Tube 2. Bring the mouth of the tube to the burner flame as you remove the stopper.

 Tube 3. Wrap the tube in a towel and bring the mouth of the tube to the burner flame as you remove the stopper. This sample is the most highly explosive of the three samples tested.

F. Solubility Tests

Test the solubility of heptane, pentene, and toluene in water by adding 1 mL (or less) of each hydrocarbon to about 5 mL portions of water in a test tube. Shake each mixture for a few seconds and note whether they are soluble. For any that are not soluble note the relative density of the hydrocarbon with respect to water.

Test the miscibility of these three hydrocarbons with each other by mixing about 1 mL of each in a **dry** test tube.

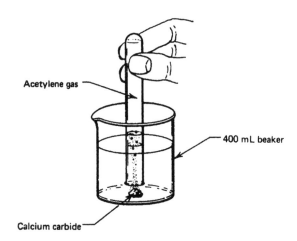

Figure 28.1   Collecting acetylene from calcium carbide-water reaction

NAME _____

SECTION _____ DATE _____

INSTRUCTOR _____

REPORT FOR EXPERIMENT 28

Hydrocarbons

A. Combustion

1. Describe the combustion characteristics of heptane and pentene.

2. (a) Write a balanced equation to represent the complete combustion of heptane.

   (b) How many moles of oxygen are needed for the combustion of 1 mole of heptane in this reaction?

   _____

B. and C. Reaction with Bromine and Potassium Permanganate

Data Table: Place an X in the column where a reaction was observed.

	Heptane (Saturated Hydrocarbon)	Pentene (Unsaturated Hydrocarbon)	Toluene (Aromatic Hydrocarbon)
Immediate reaction with Br_2 (*without* exposure to *light*)			✕
Slow reaction with Br_2 (*or only after exposure to light*)			✕
Reaction with $KMnO_4$			

1. Which of the two hydrocarbons reacted with bromine (without exposure to light)?

2. Write an equation to illustrate how heptane reacts with bromine when the reaction mixture is exposed to sunlight.

3. Write an equation to illustrate how pentene reacts with bromine. Assume the pentene is $CH_3CH_2CH{=}CHCH_3$ and use structural formulas.

4. Which of the three hydrocarbons tested gave a positive Baeyer test?

_____

D. Kerosene

1. (a) Did you observe any evidence of reaction with bromine before exposure to light? If so, describe.

   (b) Did you observe any evidence of reaction with bromine after exposure to light? If so, describe.

2. Did you observe any evidence of reaction with potassium permanganate? If so, describe.

3. Based on these tests (bromine and potassium permanganate), to which class of hydrocarbon does kerosene belong?

_____

E. Acetylene

1. Describe the combustion characteristics of acetylene:

   (a) Tube 1.

   (b) Tube 2.

   (c) Tube 3.

2. Write an equation for the complete combustion of acetylene.

F. Solubility Tests

1. Which of the three hydrocarbons tested are soluble in water?

2. From your observations what do you conclude about the density of hydrocarbons with respect to water?

QUESTIONS AND PROBLEMS

1. Do you expect that acetylene would react with bromine without exposure to light? Explain your answer.

2. Write structural formulas for the three different isomers of pentane, all having the molecular formula C_5H_{12}. See Study Aid 6 for help if necessary.

3. Write structural formulas for (a) ethene, (b) propene, and (c) the three different isomeric butenes (C_4H_8). See Study Aid 6 for help if necessary.

EXPERIMENT 29

Alcohols, Esters, Aldehydes, and Ketones

MATERIALS AND EQUIPMENT

Solids: Copper wire (No. 18, with spiral); salicylic acid [$C_6H_4(COOH)(OH)$]. **Liquids:** acetic acid, glacial (CH_3COOH); acetone [$(CH_3)_2C=O$]; ethyl alcohol (95% C_2H_5OH); isoamyl alcohol ($C_5H_{11}OH$); isopropyl alcohol (iso-C_3H_7OH); methyl alcohol (CH_3OH). **Solutions:** dilute (6 M) ammonium hydroxide (NH_4OH), 10 percent glucose ($C_6H_{12}O_6$), 10 percent formaldehyde ($H_2C=O$), 0.1 M potassium permanganate ($KMnO_4$), 0.1 M silver nitrate ($AgNO_3$), 10 percent sodium hydroxide (NaOH), and dilute (3 M) sulfuric acid (H_2SO_4).

DISCUSSION

In this experiment we will examine some of the properties and characteristic reactions of four classes of organic compounds: alcohols, esters, aldehydes, and ketones.

Alcohols

The formulas of alcohols may be derived from alkane hydrocarbon formulas by replacing a hydrogen atom with a hydroxyl group (OH). In the resulting alcohols the OH group is bonded to the carbon atom by a covalent bond and is not an ionizable hydroxide group. Examples follow:

Alkane	Alcohol	Name of Alcohol*
CH_4	CH_3OH	Methanol (Methyl alcohol)
CH_3CH_3	CH_3CH_2OH	Ethanol (Ethyl alcohol)
$CH_3CH_2CH_3$	$CH_3CH_2CH_2OH$	1-Propanol (n-Propyl alcohol)
$CH_3CH_2CH_3$	$CH_3\underset{\underset{OH}{\vert}}{C}HCH_3$	2-Propanol (Isopropyl alcohol)

*Common names in parentheses

Thus there is an entire homologous series of alcohols. The functional group of the alcohols is the hydroxyl group, OH.

Esters

This class of organic compounds may be formed by reacting alcohols with organic acids. Esters generally have a pleasant odor; many of them occur naturally, being found mainly in fruits and fatty material.

Methyl acetate will be used as an example illustrating the formation of an ester. When acetic acid and methyl alcohol are reacted together, using sulfuric acid as a catalyst, a molecule of water is split out between a molecule of the acetic acid and a molecule of the alcohol, forming the ester. The equation is

$$\underset{\text{Acetic acid}}{CH_3\overset{\displaystyle O}{\overset{\|}{C}}-OH} \; + \; \underset{\text{Methyl alcohol}}{CH_3-OH} \quad \xrightarrow[\Delta]{H_2SO_4} \quad \underset{\text{Methyl acetate}}{CH_3\overset{\displaystyle O}{\overset{\|}{C}}-O-CH_3} \; + \; H_2O$$

The functional group characterizing organic acids is

$$-\overset{\displaystyle O}{\overset{\|}{C}}-OH \qquad \text{or} \qquad -COOH$$

It is called the **carboxyl group.**

Esters are named in the following manner. The first part of the name is taken from the name of the alcohol, the second part is derived by adding the suffix ate to the identifying stem of the acid. Thus acetic becomes acetate, and the name of the ester derived from methyl alcohol and acetic acid is methyl acetate.

Aldehydes and Ketones

The functional groups of the aldehydes and ketones are

$$\underset{\text{Aldehyde}}{-\overset{\displaystyle H}{\overset{|}{C}}=O} \qquad\qquad \underset{\text{Ketone}}{R-\overset{\displaystyle}{\underset{\displaystyle O}{\overset{|}{\underset{\|}{C}}}}-R}$$

Aldehydes and ketones may be obtained by oxidizing alcohols. One major difference between aldehydes and ketones is that aldehydes are very easily oxidized to carboxylic acids, but ketones are not easily further oxidized. Thus aldehydes are good reducing agents. Chemical reactions for distinguishing aldehydes and ketones are based on this difference.

Alcohol	**Aldehyde**	**Ketone**
CH_3OH	$H-\overset{\displaystyle H}{\overset{|}{C}}=O$ Methanal (formaldehyde)	—
CH_3CH_2OH	$CH_3\overset{\displaystyle H}{\overset{|}{C}}=O$ Ethanal (acetaldehyde)	—
$CH_3CH_2CH_2OH$	$CH_3CH_2\underset{\displaystyle H}{\overset{\displaystyle C=O}{\overset{|}{}}}$ Propanal (propionaldehyde)	—
$CH_3\underset{\displaystyle OH}{\overset{|}{C}}HCH_3$	—	$CH_3\overset{\displaystyle}{\underset{\displaystyle O}{\overset{}{\underset{\|}{C}}}}CH_3$ Acetone (propanone)

175

PROCEDURE

Wear protective glasses.

> Record your observations immediately on the report form as you work through the procedure.
>
> Reagents used in this experiment are highly flammable and several are poisonous. Work cautiously away from heat and open flames, and avoid inhalation of vapors, contact with skin and clothing, and do not ingest.
>
> Dispose of all reagents in the "organic solvent" waste container provided. The symbol is used throughout this procedure to remind you of this disposal requirement.

A. Combustion of Alcohols

Obtain about 1 mL (no more) of methyl alcohol in an evaporating dish and ignite the alcohol with a match or burning splint. Repeat with equally small volumes of ethyl alcohol and isopropyl alcohol. Observe the color and luminescence of the flame.

B. Oxidation of Alcohols

1. Oxidation with Potassium Permanganate. Mix 3 mL of methyl alcohol with 12 mL of water and divide the solution into three equal portions, placing them in three test tubes. To a fourth tube add 5 mL water. Add 1 drop of 10 percent sodium hydroxide to the first tube and 1 drop of dilute sulfuric acid to the second. Now add 1 drop of potassium permanganate solution to each of the four tubes. Mix and note how long it takes for the reaction to occur in each of the first three tubes, using the fourth tube as a reference tube. Disappearance of the purple permanganate color is evidence of reaction. (Patience, some reactions take a long time.)

Repeat this oxidation procedure, using isopropyl alcohol instead of methyl alcohol.

2. Oxidation with Copper(II) Oxide. Put about 2 mL of methyl alcohol in a test tube. Obtain from the reagent shelf about a 20 cm piece of copper wire with a four- or five-turn spiral at one end. Warm the alcohol slightly to promote alcohol vapors in the tube. Heat the copper spiral in the hottest part of the burner flame to get a good copper(II) oxide coating. Do not overheat the copper or it will melt. While the copper spiral is very hot, lower it part way into the tube (not to the liquid) and note the results. Heat the wire again and lower it into the tube, finally dropping it into the liquid alcohol. Remove the wire and gently waft the vapors from the tube to your nose to detect the odor of formaldehyde resulting from the oxidation of the methyl alcohol. **Return the copper wire to the reagent shelf.**

C. Formation of Esters

Take three test tubes and mix the following reagents in them.

Tube 1: 3 mL ethyl alcohol, 0.5 mL glacial acetic acid, and 10 drops of dilute (3 M) sulfuric acid.

Tube 2: 3 mL isoamyl alcohol, 0.5 mL glacial acetic acid, and 10 drops concentrated sulfuric acid.

Tube 3: Salicylic acid crystals (about 1 cm deep in the tube), 2 mL methyl alcohol, and 10 drops concentrated sulfuric acid.

Heat the tubes by placing them in boiling water for 3 minutes.

Products formed:

Tube 1: Ethyl acetate.

Tube 2: Isoamyl acetate.

Tube 3: Methyl salicylate.

After heating, pour a small amount of each product onto a piece of filter paper and **carefully** smell it and describe the odor. [WASTE DISPOSE OF PROPERLY] Dispose of the filter paper in the solid trash.

D. Tollens Test for Aldehydes

This test is based on the ability of the aldehyde group to reduce silver ion in solution, forming either a black deposit of free silver or a silver mirror. The aldehyde group is oxidized to an acid in the reaction. Tollens reagent is made by reacting silver nitrate solution with 10% NaOH and dilute NH_4OH. Rinse all glass equipment with distilled water before use.

1. Preparation of Tollens Reagent: **Thoroughly** clean three test tubes. To 8 mL of 0.1 M silver nitrate solution in one of these tubes add one drop of 10% NaOH to generate a brown precipitate of silver oxide. Now add dilute ammonium hydroxide 1 drop at a time until the brown precipitate of silver oxide that was formed just dissolves (mix after each drop is added). Now add 7 mL of distilled water, mix, and divide the solution (Tollens reagent) equally among the three test tubes.

2. To the tubes containing the freshly prepared Tollens reagent, add the following and mix.

Tube 1: 2 drops 10% formaldehyde

Tube 2: 2 drops acetone

Tube 3: 5 drops 10% glucose

Allow the tubes to stand undisturbed and note the results. The solution containing the glucose may take 10 to 15 minutes to react. [WASTE DISPOSE OF PROPERLY] Dispose of the solutions in all three test tubes in the heavy metals waste container.

REPORT FOR EXPERIMENT 29

Alcohols, Esters, Aldehydes, and Ketones

A. Combustion of Alcohols

1. Compare the combustion characteristics of methyl, ethyl, and isopropyl alcohols, in terms of color and luminosity of their flames.

2. What type of flame would you predict for the combustion of amyl alcohol ($C_5H_{11}OH$)?

3. Write and balance the equation for the complete combustion of ethyl alcohol.

B. Oxidation of Alcohols

1. Oxidation with Potassium Permanganate

(a) Time required for oxidation of methyl alcohol by potassium permanganate:

Tube 1: Alkaline solution.   _____

Tube 2: Acid solution.   _____

Tube 3: Neutral solution.   _____

Tube 4: Water   _____

(b) Time required for oxidation of isopropyl alcohol by potassium permanganate:

Tube 1: Alkaline solution.   _____

Tube 2: Acid solution.   _____

Tube 3: Neutral solution.   _____

Tube 4: Water   _____

(c) Balance the equation for the oxidation of methyl alcohol:

$$CH_3OH + \quad KMnO_4 \longrightarrow H_2C{=}O + \quad KOH + \quad H_2O + \quad MnO_2$$

2. Oxidation with Copper(II) Oxide

(a) Write the equation for the oxidation reaction that occurred on the copper spiral when it was heated.

(b) What evidence of oxidation or reduction did you observe when the heated Cu spiral was lowered into methyl alcohol vapors?

(c) Write and balance the oxidation-reduction equation between methyl alcohol and copper(II) oxide.

C. Formation of Esters

1. Describe the odor of:

   (a) Ethyl acetate.

   (b) Isoamyl acetate.

   (c) Methyl salicylate.

2. Write an equation to illustrate the formation of ethyl acetate from ethyl alcohol and acetic acid.

3. (a) The formula for isoamyl alcohol is $CH_3CH(CH_3)CH_2CH_2OH$. Write the formula for isoamyl acetate.

(b) The formula for salicylic acid is

Write the formula for methyl salicylate.

D. Tollens Test for Aldehydes

1. How is a positive Tollens test recognized?

2. Which of the substances tested gave a positive Tollens test?

3. Circle the formula(s) of the compounds listed that will give a positive Tollens test:

$$CH_3OH \qquad C_2H_5OH \qquad CH_3\overset{H}{\underset{}{C}}=O \qquad CH_3\overset{}{\underset{\overset{\|}{O}}{C}}CH_3 \qquad Na_2CO_3$$

4. Write the formula for the oxidation product formed from formaldehyde in the Tollens test.

QUESTIONS AND PROBLEMS

1. There are four butyl alcohols of formula C_4H_9OH. Write their condensed structural formulas.

2. Write the name of the ester that can be derived from the following pairs of acids and alcohols:

Alcohol	Acid	Ester
Methyl alcohol	Acetic acid	
Ethyl alcohol	Formic acid	
Isopropyl alcohol	Butyric acid	

3. Write condensed structural formulas for all the aldehyde and ketone isomers having the molecular formula $C_5H_{10}O$.

EXPERIMENT 31

Synthesis of Aspirin

MATERIALS AND EQUIPMENT

Solids: Salicylic acid ($HO - C_6H_4 - COOH$), ice. **Liquids:** Acetic anhydride [$(CH_3CO)_2O$], ethyl alcohol (C_2H_5OH), mineral oil, 85% phosphoric acid (H_3PO_4). Büchner funnel and suction flask, rubber (heavy wall) suction tubing, melting point capillary tubes, filter paper to fit the Büchner funnel.

DISCUSSION

Aspirin (acetylsalicylic acid, or A.S.A.) is a drug that is widely used for self-medication. The familiar aspirin tablet contains 5 grains (about 325 milligrams) of acetylsalicylic acid and a small amount of an inert binding material such as starch. More than four million pounds of aspirin is manufactured each year in the United States. As a drug, aspirin has analgesic, antipyretic, and anti-inflammatory properties; that is, it can relieve pain, lower fever, and reduce inflammation.

Aspirin belongs to a group of drugs called salicylates because of their structural relationship to salicylic acid (SA),

Salicylic acid

Salicylic acid is both an aromatic carboxylic acid and a phenol. Aspirin is represented by this structural formula:

Acetylsalicylic acid (Aspirin)

This formula shows that aspirin is an ester formed between acetic acid and the phenol $-$ OH group of salicylic acid. Aspirin is a weak acid because of its carboxyl group. Acetylsalicylic acid is practically insoluble in cold water (1 g in 300 g H_2O), but its sodium salt is soluble in water.

Although it is clearly a derivative of salicylic and acetic acids, aspirin usually is not made from these substances. It can be prepared by reacting either acetyl chloride or acetic anhydride with salicylic acid. Generally, acetic anhydride, the acid anhydride of acetic acid, is used in the synthesis. Phosphoric acid catalyzes the reaction.

Salicylic acid	Acetic anhydride	Acetylsalicylic acid	Acetic acid
Molar mass = 138.1	(Ethanoic anhydride)	(Salicylyl ethanoate)	(Ethanoic acid)
	Molar mass = 102.1	Molar mass = 180.2	Molar mass = 60.05

Aspirin can be removed from the reaction mixture by adding cold water and filtering out the precipitated aspirin. The crude aspirin crystals are contaminated with small amounts of impurities, chiefly acetic and phosphoric acids. These impurities can be removed by recrystallization of the aspirin. To accomplish this, the crude aspirin is dissolved in hot alcohol, water is added, and the mixture is cooled. The crystals that form are filtered from the solution and dried to yield a product of high purity.

Why are we using acetic anhydride in this reaction and not the more abundant and less costly acetic acid? As noted above, in this experiment the phenolic group of salicylic acid is reacted with the acetyl $\left(CH_3C \overset{O}{\diagdown} \right)$ group of acetic acid to produce aspirin. However, notice that salicylic acid has both a phenolic group and a carboxylic acid group. The phenolic group of one salicylic acid molecule could react with the carboxylic acid group of another salicylic acid molecule to produce a "dimer" side-product and not the desired aspirin product.

"dimer" side-product

To minimize the production of the "dimer" side-product, acetic anhydride is utilized in place of acetic acid. Acetic anhydride is more reactive than acetic acid and thus minimizes the amount of "dimer" side-product by quickly consuming the salicylic acid before much can react with itself.

Yields in Organic Synthesis

In an organic synthesis the actual amount of finished product is almost always less—often a great deal less—than the amount theoretically obtained from the reactants used. Incomplete reactions or side reactions, that is, reactions that do not produce the desired product, can reduce the amount of product obtained. In addition, losses invariably occur in the recovery and purification steps (crystallization and recrystallization in this case). Thus, the percent of the theoretical amount of product actually obtained, or percentage yield, is a number that can be used to judge the success of a synthesis. It is calculated by this formula:

$$\text{Percentage yield} = \frac{\text{Actual mass of product obtained}}{\text{Theoretical mass of product obtainable}} \times 100$$

PROCEDURE

 Wear protective glasses.

Step 1. Accurately weigh and transfer to a 125 mL **dry** Erlenmeyer flask 3.00 g of salicylic acid. Next add 6 mL of acetic anhydride and 5 to 8 drops of 85% phosphoric acid to the flask. Swirl the flask gently to mix the reagents and place it in a beaker of warm (70–80°C) water for 15 minutes.

Step 2. Then, while the reaction mixture in the flask is still warm, **carefully** add, drop by drop, 20 drops of cold water from a medicine dropper to destroy the excess acetic anhydride.

 CAUTION: The vigorous reaction of the excess acetic anhydride with water may cause splattering.

Step 3. Add 20 mL of water to the flask; then put the flask in an ice bath to cool the reaction mixture and speed the crystallization of aspirin. When the crystallization seems to be complete, collect the crystals by suction filtration using a small Büchner funnel (Fig. 31.1) or an alternate filtering device. Wash the crystals on the filter once with a few millimeters of cold, preferably iced, water.

Step 4. Recrystallization: Transfer the crystals to a 100 mL beaker, add 10 mL of ethyl alcohol and stir to dissolve. If necessary warm the beaker in a 250 mL beaker containing warm water to complete the solution formation. When all of the crystals have dissolved, pour 25 mL of warm (60–70°C) water into the alcohol solution. Cover the beaker with a watch glass and set aside to cool until crystals begin to form. Then place the beaker in an ice bath for about 10 minutes to complete crystallization.

Step 5. After crystallization is complete, filter the crystals using the Büchner funnel suction filter. Spread the crystals out on the filter with a spatula and press them with dry filter paper to aid in drying. Transfer the crystals to a watch glass, cover with filter paper and finish drying by storing in your locker for at least one day.

Step 6. Transfer the dried aspirin to a weighed vial or test tube. Then reweigh and determine the mass of aspirin.

Step 7. Determine the melting point of your dried aspirin crystals using the method given in Experiment 27. Look up the melting point given for aspirin in the chemical literature. The *Handbook of Chemistry and Physics or Lange's Handbook of Chemistry* are suitable sources.

 Dispose of all solutions down the drain.

Hand in (properly labeled) or dispose of the product as directed by your instructor. Your label should contain your name, name of product, mass of product, and percent yield.

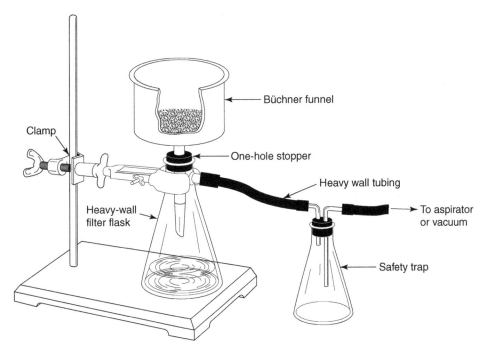

Figure 31.1 Büchner Funnel Setup

REPORT FOR EXPERIMENT 31

Synthesis of Aspirin

Percentage yield of aspirin

1. Mass of salicylic acid used   _____

2. Mass of aspirin crystals obtained   _____

3. Mass of aspirin theoretically obtainable from
   salicylic acid used. Show calculation setup.   _____

4. Percentage yield of aspirin based on theoretical
   mass from 3. Show calculation setup.   _____

Melting point:

1. Melting point range of your aspirin   _____

2. Melting point of aspirin from the literature   _____

QUESTIONS AND PROBLEMS

1. Write the chemical equation representing the synthesis of aspirin from acetyl chloride.

2. Could aspirin be prepared by the method used in this experiment from these compounds? Explain your answer.

3. (a) How many moles of acetic anhydride were represented by the 6.00 mL (density = 1.08 g/mL) used in the synthesis? (b) How many excess moles of acetic anhydride were used-over and above the amount needed to react with 3.00 g of salicylic acid? Show calculations.

(a) _____

(b) _____

4. Aspirin is insoluble in water. Explain why it is soluble in sodium hydroxide solution.

5. If the annual production of acetyl salicylic acid in the U.S.A. were converted to 5-grain aspirin tablets, approximately how many tablets would there be for each person? Assume that the population is about 3.0×10^8. Show calculation.

_____

6. What is (a) an analgesic and (b) an antipyretic?

EXPERIMENT 32

Amines and Amides

MATERIALS AND EQUIPMENT

Solids: Urea (CH_4N_2O), ethanamide (acetamide, C_2H_5NO), 1-naphthol (α-naphthol, $C_{10}H_8O$), *p*-nitroaniline, ($C_6H_6N_2O_2$), sodium nitrite ($NaNO_2$). **Liquids:** concentrated ammonium hydroxide (NH_4OH), aniline (C_6H_7N), pyridine (C_5H_5N), diethylamine ($C_4H_{11}N$), n-hexylamine ($C_6H_{13}NH_2$), **Solutions:** 6 M HCl, 3 M H_2SO_4, 1 M NaOH. Ice bath.

DISCUSSION

Many organic and biological molecules contain nitrogen. Amines and amides are two such nitrogen-containing molecules.

A. Amines

In general, **amines** can be thought of as ammonia (NH_3) in which the hydrogens have been removed and replaced by organic "R"-groups (aromatic or aliphatic) to produce primary (1°), secondary (2°), and tertiary amines (3°).

RNH_2	R_2NH	R_3H
1°	2°	3°

Since the nitrogen atom in an amine has an unshared pair of electrons, a fourth R-group can be added to produce a positively charged quarternary (4°) ammonium salt.

$$R_3N + RCl \rightarrow R_4N^+Cl^- \quad \text{(quaternary ammonium salt)}$$

Examples of amines include:

$CH_3CH_2NH_2$

aminoethane (1°)
(ethylamine)

$CH_3CH_2{-}N(H){-}CH_3$

ethylmethylamine (2°)

$(H_3C)_2N{-}CH_2CH_2CH_3$

dimethylpropylamine (3°)

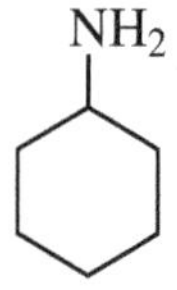

aminocyclohexane
(cyclohexylamine)

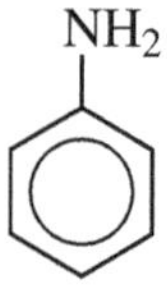

aniline

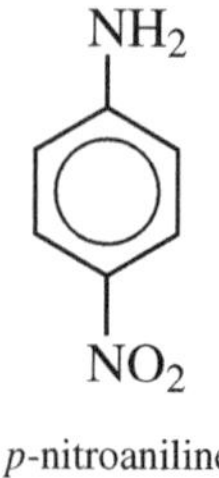

p-nitroaniline

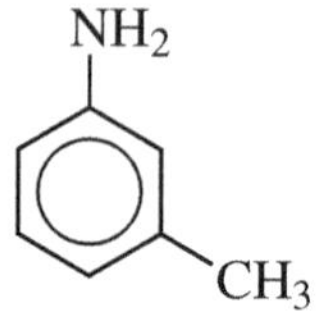

m-methylaniline

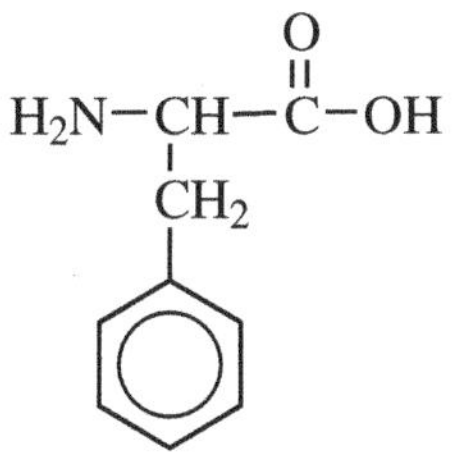

phenylalanine
(one of the twenty common amino acids)

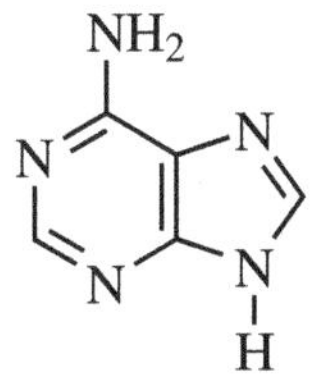

adenine
(a purine)

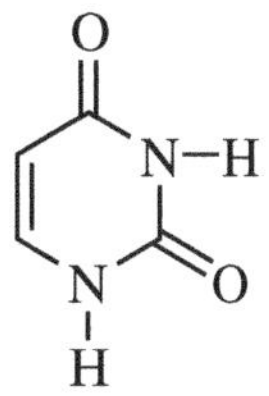

uracil
(a pyrimidine)

Amines are basic substances and can be protonated, in acid, to form positively charged substituted ammonium ions.

$$RNH_2 + H^+ \longrightarrow RNH_3^+$$

$$R_2NH + H^+ \longrightarrow R_2NH_2^+$$

$$R_3N + H^+ \longrightarrow R_3NH^+$$

Even water is acidic enough to protonate ammonia and many amines. For example

$$NH_3 + H_2O \rightleftharpoons NH_4^+ + OH^-$$

$$RNH_2 + H_2O \rightleftharpoons RNH_3^+ + OH^-$$

Due to their hydrogen bonding ability, aliphatic amines containing up to five carbons are quite soluble in water. Aromatic amines are considerably less soluble than aliphatic amines. Both the size and the number of R-groups attached to the nitrogen atom affect the solubility of amines in water. Generally, solubility decreases with larger R-groups and with increased numbers of R-groups attached to the nitrogen.

Amines are utilized as starting materials in many medical and commercial chemical syntheses. One such starting material is aniline. Also, substituted aniline derivatives such as m, and p-nitroanilines can be used. Several important dyes can be produced by reacting aniline with sodium nitrite to yield a diazonium salt, which is then reacted with a suitable reactant such as phenol and similar compounds. These syntheses generally employ a diazonium salt as a critical intermediate.

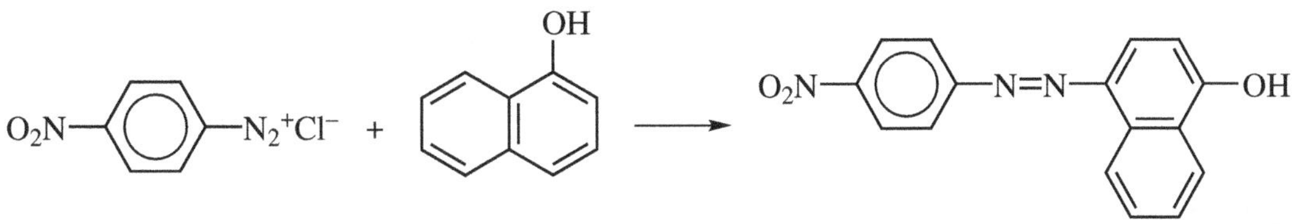

diazonium salt
(p-nitrobenzene
diazonium chloride)

1-naphthol

final "coupled" dye

B. Amides

Amides are neutral nitrogen-containing compounds in which the nitrogen is bonded directly to a carbonyl carbon. Mono- or disubstituted amides have one or two R-groups instead of H on the $-NH_2$ group.

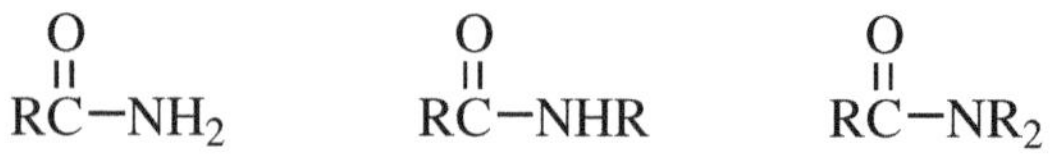

$$\underset{RC-NH_2}{\overset{\overset{\textstyle O}{\|}}{}} \qquad \underset{RC-NHR}{\overset{\overset{\textstyle O}{\|}}{}} \qquad \underset{RC-NR_2}{\overset{\overset{\textstyle O}{\|}}{}}$$

Examples of amides include:

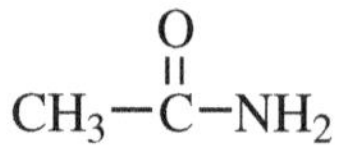

acetamide
(ethanamide)   N-methylethanamide 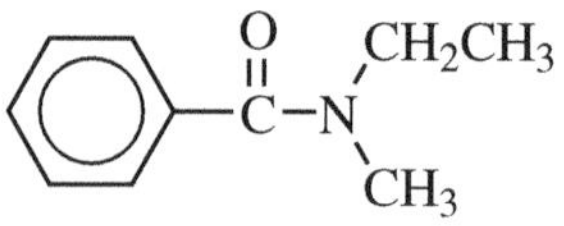   N-ethyl-N-methylbenzamide

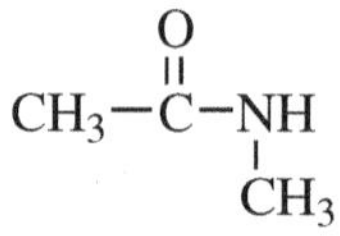

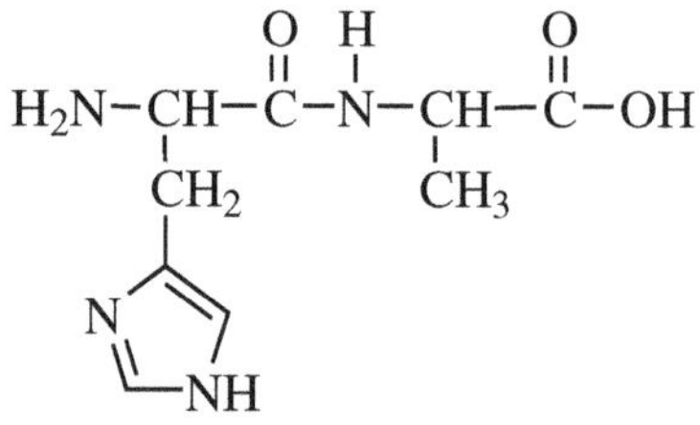

histidylalanine (a dipeptide)

Simple amides can be synthesized by reacting a carboxylic acid with ammonia to produce an ammonium salt and then heating the ammonium salt to generate the corresponding amide.

$$RCOOH + NH_3 \longrightarrow RCOO^-NH_4^+$$

$$RCOO^-NH_4^+ \overset{\Delta}{\longrightarrow} RCONH_2 + H_2O$$

Amides are hydrolyzed under acid conditions to yield a carboxylic acid and an ammonium salt. Under basic conditions the products are the salt of a carboxylic acid and ammonia or an amine.

$$RCONH_2 + H_2O + HCl \longrightarrow RCOOH + NH_4Cl$$

$$RCONH_2 + H_2O + NaOH \longrightarrow RCOO^-Na^+ + NH_3$$

PROCEDURE

Wear protective glasses.

A. Amine Solubility and Acidity Tests

1. Clean and label five (5) test tubes. Place about 1 mL of the following amines in each test tube (one amine per test tube): (1) concentrated ammonium hydroxide; (2) aniline; (3) pyridine; (4) diethylamine; (5) n-hexylamine. Add approximately 4 mL of water to each test tube and **thoroughly** mix. Record your results concerning the solubility of each amine.

2. Using pH indicator paper, test the pH of the water layer (be sure you understand which layer, if any, is the water layer) in each of the above test tubes. Record your results.

3. Add 1 mL of 6 M HCl to each of the above test tubes. **Thoroughly** mix each test tube. Concerning solubility, record your results. Again using pH indicator paper, test for pH in each water layer and record your results.

 Dispose of the residue in each test tube in the organic waste container.

B. Amide Hydrolysis

1. Clean a test tube and add approximately 1 gram of urea. Now add about 5 mL of 3 M H_2SO_4 and thoroughly mix. Heat the mixture in a boiling water bath. After about five minutes in the boiling water bath, **carefully** note any odor coming from the test tube.

2. Clean a test tube and add approximately 1 gram of ethanamide (acetamide). Now add about 5 mL of 3 M H_2SO_4 and thoroughly mix. Heat the mixture in a boiling water bath. After about five minutes in the boiling water bath, **carefully** note any odor coming from the test tube. Add sufficient 3 M H_2SO_4 to acidify the mixture (use either pH indicator paper or litmus paper to verify that the mixture is acidic). Record what you observe upon addition of the acid.

 Dispose of the residues in the organic waste container.

C. Synthesis of a Nitrogen-Containing Dye Via a Diazonium Intermediate

NOTE: The following reactions must be kept cold in an ice bath at all times because diazonium salts are unstable.

1. Using a suitably sized plastic trough, fill the trough with ice/water for use as an ice bath. Be sure there is sufficient water to allow the containers used in the reaction to be surrounded with ice/water, but not so much water as to permit the containers to tip and mix with the ice/water.

2. Prepare the following solutions and keep them in the ice bath.

Solution 1: In a 50 mL beaker place 0.3 gram of 1-naphthol. Add 15 mL of 1.0 M sodium hydroxide. Mix and keep cold.

Solution 2: In an ice-bath-cooled 50 mL flask place 0.5 gram of p-nitroaniline. Add 10 mL of water. Add 1 mL of 6 M HCl and thoroughly mix. Keep cold.

Solution 3: In a test tube place 0.5 gram of sodium nitrite. Add 3 mL of water to the test tube and dissolve the sodium nitrite by stirring the mixture. Keep cold.

3. To the flask containing the p-nitroaniline, add the sodium nitrite solution. While still in the ice bath, thoroughly stir the combined solutions to generate the diazonium salt.

Add the diazonium salt containing solution that you just made to the beaker containing the 1-naphthol. Keep in the ice bath and stir. Record your results.

 Dispose of the residue in the organic waste container.

NAME ______________________

SECTION __________ DATE __________

REPORT FOR EXPERIMENT 32

INSTRUCTOR ______________________

Amines and Amides

A. Amine Solubility and Acidity Tests

SOLUBILITY *BEFORE* ADDITION OF ACID

Results for Test Tube 1 ______________________

Results for Test Tube 2 ______________________

Results for Test Tube 3 ______________________

Results for Test Tube 4 ______________________

Results for Test Tube 5 ______________________

pH RESULTS *BEFORE* ADDITION OF ACID

pH for Test Tube 1 ______________________

pH for Test Tube 2 ______________________

pH for Test Tube 3 ______________________

pH for Test Tube 4 ______________________

pH for Test Tube 5 ______________________

SOLUBILITY *AFTER* ADDITION OF ACID

Results for Test Tube 1 _____

Results for Test Tube 2 _____

Results for Test Tube 3 _____

Results for Test Tube 4 _____

Results for Test Tube 5 _____

pH RESULTS *AFTER* ADDITION OF ACID

pH for Test Tube 1 _____

pH for Test Tube 2 _____

pH for Test Tube 3 _____

pH for Test Tube 4 _____

pH for Test Tube 5 _____

1. List the amines that are insoluble in water?

2. Did the addition of HCl change the solubilities and why?

3. Can you make any conclusions about amine structure and solubility? What are those conclusions?

4. Which amine is most acidic and why?

5. Which amine is most basic and why?

6. Did the addition of HCl change the pH of the water layers and why?

B.   Amide Hydrolysis

1. For the urea reaction with H_2SO_4 describe the odor coming from the heated test tube. What chemical do you theorize as causing the odor?

2. What occurred upon addition of H_2SO_4 to the acetamide solution?

3. Write a balanced equation for the addition of H_2SO_4 to the heated acetamide solution.

C.   Synthesis of a Nitrogen-Containing Dye

1. What did you observe when you added the diazonium salt to the 1-naphthol?

2. If the combined diazonium salt and 1-naphthol had been reacted at room temperature, would the colored product have been produced? Why?

QUESTIONS AND PROBLEMS

1. Write a balanced equation for the protonation of pyridine by HCl.

2. Using the *Handbook of Chemistry and Physics* and/or the *Merck Index* (or other appropriate reference book) give solubility data in water and ethanol for the compounds you used in this experiment.

ammonium hydroxide

aniline

pyridine

diethylamine

n-hexylamine

p-nitroaniline

3. Write a balanced equation for the acidic hydrolysis of propanamide by HCl.

4. Write a balanced equation for the basic hydrolysis of butanamide by KOH.

5. What would occur if you had mixed the diazonium salt with 2-naphthol instead of 1-naphthol? (A structural formula might be helpful in your explanation.)

EXPERIMENT 34

Carbohydrates

MATERIALS AND EQUIPMENT

Solids: Glucose, sucrose. **Liquids:** Concentrated sulfuric acid. **Solutions:** 1% solutions of arabinose, fructose, glucose, maltose, starch, sucrose (freshly prepared), and xylose; concentrated hydrochloric acid, 1% iodine in 2% potassium iodide (I_2-KI); 10% sodium hydroxide; reagent solutions for Barfoed, Benedict, Bial, Molisch, and Seliwanoff tests; fruit juices such as orange, lemon, lime, grapefruit, apple, etc.

DISCUSSION

Carbohydrates are one of the three principal classes of foods. They are major constituents of plants and are also found in animal tissues. They were so named because the carbon, hydrogen, and oxygen atom ratio in most carbohydrates approximates that of $C \cdot H_2O$. Carbohydrates, of course, are not hydrates of carbon but are relatively complex substances such as sugars, starches, and cellulose. Chemically, **carbohydrates** are polyhydroxy aldehydes or ketones or substances that, when hydrolyzed, yield polyhydroxyl aldehydes or ketones.

Carbohydrates are classified as monosaccharides, disaccharides, oligosaccharides, or polysaccharides based on the number of monosaccharide units present in the molecule. A **monosaccharide** is a carbohydrate that cannot be hydrolyzed to simpler carbohydrate molecules. A **disaccharide** yields 2 monosaccharide molecules, alike or different, when hydrolyzed. **Oligosaccharides,** on hydrolysis, yield 2 to 10 monosaccharide molecules. The monosaccharide molecule may be of only one kind, or they may be of two or more different kinds. **Polysaccharides,** when hydrolyzed, yield many monosaccharide molecules. These monosaccharide molecules are typically of only one kind.

The monosaccharides are further classified according to the length of the carbon chain, such as trioses ($C_3H_6O_3$), tetroses ($C_4H_8O_4$), pentoses ($C_5H_{10}O_5$), and hexoses ($C_6H_{12}O_6$). If they are aldehydes, they are called aldoses; if ketones, they are called ketoses. The most common monosaccharides are glucose, galactose, and fructose. Glucose and galactose are aldohexoses; fructose is a ketohexose. The three common disaccharides are sucrose (glucose and fructose), maltose (glucose and glucose), and lactose (galactose and glucose). All three have the formula $C_{12}H_{22}O_{11}$ and can be hydrolyzed to yield their respective monosaccharides by heating in a water solution containing a small amount of HCl or H_2SO_4. The three most common polysaccharides, starch, glycogen, and cellulose, have the formula $(C_6H_{10}O_5)_n$, where n ranges from about 200 to several thousand. All three are polymers of glucose.

Numerous tests have been devised for determination of the properties and for the differentiation of carbohydrates. A brief description of some of these tests follows:

Molisch Test

This is a very general test for carbohydrates. The test is based on the formation of furfural, or hydroxyfurfural when a carbohydrate reacts with concentrated sulfuric acid. The furfural reacts with the Molisch reagent, α-naphthol, to yield colored condensation products.

Seliwanoff Test

This test distinguishes fructose, a ketohexose, from aldohexoses and disaccharides. The reaction between fructose and the reagent (resorcinol in dilute HCl) occurs within one minute in boiling water. A reddish-colored product is formed; the color intensifies with further heating. Other carbohydrates subjected to this test will produce a faint red color if heating is prolonged. The color formation is attributable to transformation of glucose to fructose by the catalytic action of hydrochloric acid or by hydrolysis of sucrose to yield fructose.

Benedict Test

The Benedict test and Barfoed test are reduction tests. Certain carbohydrates have a reducing ability because they have, or are able to form, a free aldehyde or ketone group in solution. In alkaline solution, copper(II) or silver ions are reduced to characteristic precipitates of Cu_2O or free Ag. All the common monosaccharides are reducing sugars. Some disaccharides and polysaccharides may initially be nonreducing but show reducing properties after heating in an acidic solution. During the heating, hydrolysis to monosaccharides occurs. Some widely used tests for sugars are based on this reducing ability of carbohydrates. An example is the Benedict test, which is used to detect sugar (glucose) in urine.

In the Benedict test Cu^{2+} is reduced to Cu^+, forming Cu_2O, which is a brick-red colored precipitate. However, the color in a positive Benedict test may appear as green, yellow, orange, or red depending upon the amount of Cu_2O suspended in the dark blue reagent. The amount of Cu_2O formed depends on the concentration of sugar in the solution. Reducing sugars give a positive test.

Barfoed Test

The Barfoed reagent is used to distinguish between mono- and disaccharides. This test is also a copper reduction reaction but differs from the Benedict test in that the reagent is made in an acidic medium [copper(II) acetate and acetic acid]. Within the stated time interval, only monosaccharides will reduce the Cu^{2+} ions. If heated long enough, disaccharides will be hydrolyzed by the acid present and give a positive test. Barfoed reagent is not suitable for detection of sugar in urine.

Bial Test

This test is used to distinguish pentoses from hexoses. Pentoses occur in both plants and animals. The pentoses ribose and deoxyribose are universally found in the nucleic acid portion of nucleoproteins of the cells. Bial reagent contains orcinol (5-methylresorcinol) dissolved in concentrated HCl plus a small amount of $FeCl_3$. When mixed with the reagent, pentoses are converted to furfural, which reacts to yield a blue-green colored compound.

Iodine Test

Iodine reacts with starch to form a deep blue complex. When an acidified starch solution is boiled, it hydrolyzes to yield glucose ultimately. The blue color in the iodine test can be used to follow the course of this hydrolysis.

PROCEDURE

 Wear protective glasses.

 Dispose of all materials in the containers provided.

A. Molisch Test

Run this test on each of the following 1% carbohydrate solutions and on water as a reference blank: (1) arabinose, (2) glucose, (3) fructose, (4) maltose, (5) sucrose, (6) starch, and (7) water (blank). To 5 mL of the carbohydrate solution in a test tube, add 3 drops of Molisch reagent and mix well. Now tilt the test tube at an angle of about 45 degrees and very carefully and slowly pour 2-3 mL of concentrated sulfuric acid from a 10 mL graduated cylinder down the side of the test tube so that the sulfuric acid forms a layer underneath the solution being tested.

 NOTE: It is very important that the lip of the graduated cylinder be touching the inner top of the test tube containing the carbohydrate and that the **acid be poured slowly.**

Set the test tubes in the rack and observe for evidence of reaction at the interface of the two liquid layers. Some reactions may take as long as 15 to 20 minutes, so proceed with the next part of the experiment.

B. Seliwanoff Test

Run this test on each of the following solutions: (1) arabinose, (2) glucose, (3) fructose, (4) maltose, (5) sucrose, and (6) water (blank). Mix together in a test tube 1 mL of the carbohydrate solution and 4 mL of Seliwanoff reagent. Place all six tubes in a beaker of boiling water for 2 minutes. (Do not overheat.) Observe and record the results.

C. Benedict Test

Run this test on each of the following solutions: (1) arabinose, (2) glucose, (3) fructose, (4) maltose, (5) sucrose, (6) starch, and (7) water (blank). Mix together in a test tube 1 mL of the carbohydrate solution and 5 mL of Benedict reagent. Place all seven tubes in a beaker of boiling water for 5 minutes. Observe and record the results.

D. Barfoed Test

Run this test on each of the following solutions: (1) arabinose, (2) glucose, (3) maltose, (4) sucrose, and (5) water (blank). Mix together in a test tube 1 mL of the carbohydrate solution and 5 mL of Barfoed reagent. Place all the tubes in a beaker of boiling water for 5 minutes. Observe and record the results.

E. Bial Test

Run this test on each of the following solutions: (1) arabinose, (2) xylose, (3) glucose, (4) fructose, and (5) water (blank). Mix together in a test tube 2 mL of the carbohydrate solution and

3 mL of Bial reagent. Carefully heat (with agitation) each tube over a burner flame until the mixture just begins to boil. Observe and record the results.

F. Dehydration

1. Place about 2 grams (no more) of sucrose in a test tube; add 1 mL of concentrated sulfuric acid. After about 30 seconds **very carefully** touch the test tube to feel the heat evolved. Observe and record the results. Allow the tube to cool for about ten minutes. Successively add and pour out small amounts of water to loosen the residue in the tube.

 Dispose of the black residue in the waste container provided.

2. Repeat this experiment using about 2 grams of glucose and 1 mL concentrated sulfuric acid.

G. Hydrolysis of Disaccharides

Mix together 10 mL of sucrose solution and 5 drops of concentrated hydrochloric acid in one test tube and, in a second test tube, 10 mL of maltose solution and 5 drops of concentrated hydrochloric acid. Place both tubes in a beaker of boiling water for about 10 minutes. Cool the solutions and neutralize the acid with 10% NaOH solution (requires 18-20 drops of base). Use red litmus paper as an indicator. Now run Benedict and Seliwanoff tests using 2 mL samples of the hydrolyzed sugar solutions and 5 mL of each test reagent. Record your results.

H. Hydrolysis of Starch

Mix together in a 100 mL beaker 10 mL of 1% starch solution, 20 mL of water, and 10 drops of concentrated hydrochloric acid. Label five clean test tubes as (1) blank, (2) reference, (3) 5 minutes, (4) 10 minutes, and (5) 15 minutes. Add a medicine dropper full of distilled water to tube (1). Withdraw one medicine dropper full of the starch solution and put it in tube (2). Save these two samples for later reference.

Cover the beaker with a watch glass and gently boil the starch solution for 15 minutes. (Consider the zero time when the solution first starts to boil.) During the boiling period withdraw a medicine dropper full of the hot solution every 5 minutes and transfer the solution to the appropriate test tubes, (3), (4), and (5). Now add 1 drop of the I_2—KI solution to each of the five tubes and mix. Record your observations.

After the heating is completed, withdraw another medicine dropper full of the solution and transfer it to a test tube. Neutralize the acid present with 10% NaOH solution and test for the presence of a reducing sugar with Benedict reagent.

I. Fruit Juices

Test available fruit juices (preferably fresh), e.g., orange, lemon, lime, grapefruit, apple, etc., for the presence of reducing sugars and fructose using Benedict and Seliwanoff reagents. Use about 1 mL samples of juice for each test.

INSTRUCTOR DEMONSTRATION (OPTIONAL)

Colloidal Nature of Starch

Mix 5 mL of 1% starch suspension with 200 mL distilled water, divide into two equal portions and place them into 100 mL beakers. Fill a third 100 mL beaker with distilled water, align the three beakers with the water in the center and pass a narrow beam of light from a microscope illuminator (or other higher intensity source) through the beakers. Note the marked Tyndall effect apparent in even this very dilute starch. Observe the suspension from both the side and top views.

 Dispose of the starch solution down the sink drain.

NAME ____________________

SECTION ________ DATE ________

REPORT FOR EXPERIMENT 34

INSTRUCTOR ____________________

Carbohydrates

A. Molisch Test

1. Describe the evidence for a positive test.

2. What is the chemical basis for a positive test?

3. Circle the names of the substances that gave a positive test.

   arabinose   glucose   fructose   maltose   sucrose   starch   water

B. Selinwanoff test

1. Describe the evidence for a positive test.

2. Circle the name(s) of the substances that gave a positive test.

   arabinose   glucose   fructose   maltose   sucrose   water

3. Upon prolonged heating, would you expect sucrose to give a positive Seliwanoff test? Explain.

C. Benedict Test

1. Describe the evidence for a positive test.

2. Circle the name(s) of the substances tested that gave a positive Benedict test.

   arabinose   glucose   fructose   maltose   sucrose   starch   water

3. Circle the name(s) of the substances tested that are reducing carbohydrates.

   arabinose   glucose   fructose   maltose   sucrose   starch

4. If the Cu^{2+} ions in Benedict reagent are reduced, what must have happened to the sugar molecules?

5. Complete and balance:

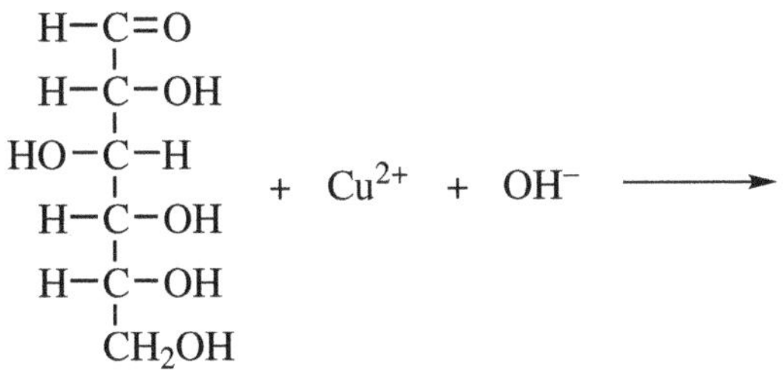

$$
\begin{array}{l}
H-C=O \\
H-C-OH \\
HO-C-H \\
H-C-OH \\
H-C-OH \\
CH_2OH
\end{array}
+ \; Cu^{2+} \; + \; OH^- \longrightarrow
$$

D. Barfoed Test

1. What is the evidence for a positive test?

2. Circle the name(s) of the substances tested that gave a positive Barfoed test.

   arabinose   glucose   maltose   sucrose   water

3. How is Barfoed reagent able to distinguish a reducing monosaccharide from a reducing disaccharide?

4. Circle the name(s) of any of the following carbohydrates that will give a positive Barfoed test.

   ribose   lactose   mannose   starch

E. Bial test

1. What is the evidence for a positive test?

2. Circle the name(s) of the substances that gave a positive Bial test.

   arabinose   xylose   glucose   fructose   water

3. Write the structural formulas of two carbohydrates (other than those tested) that will give a positive Bial test.

F. Dehydration

1. Describe the effects that you noted after the addition of concentrated sulfuric acid to sucrose.

2. Write an equation for the reaction of sucrose with sulfuric acid. Assume complete dehydration and the formation of $H_2SO_4 \cdot H_2O$ as one of the products.

G. Hydrolysis of Disaccharides

1. Results after hydrolysis. Use + or − signs to indicate whether the test was positive or negative.

	Sucrose	**Maltose**
Benedict Test	_____	_____
Seliwanoff Test	_____	_____

2. What do the results of these tests indicate about the composition of sucrose and maltose?

H. Hydrolysis of Starch

1. What is the evidence for a positive iodine test for starch?

2. What evidence did you observe to indicate that the starch was hydrolyzing while being heated?

3. Did the Benedict tests prove that the starch actually was hydrolyzed? Explain.

I.   Fruit Juices

1. Tabulate your results using + or − signs to indicate whether a positive or a negative result was obtained with each fruit juice tested.

Fruit Juice	Benedict Test	Seliwanoff Test

2. Which carbohydrate(s) is proven to be present in each fruit juice tested?

QUESTIONS AND PROBLEMS

1. The possible carbohydrates in the following problems are limited to these: arabinose, glucose, fructose, maltose, sucrose, and starch.

 (a) A carbohydrate solution gave a positive Molisch test and negative Benedict, Barfoed, Bial, and Seliwanoff tests. When treated with hydrochloric acid and boiled for several minutes, the solution showed positive Benedict, Barfoed, and Seliwanoff tests and a negative Bial test. Which carbohydrate was in the original solution?

 (b) A solution containing only one carbohydrate gave a Cu_2O precipitate with Benedict reagent. Which of the carbohydrates is present in the solution?

 (c) Another sample of the solution from (b) failed to give a Cu_2O precipitate with Barfoed reagent. Which carbohydrate is present in the solution?

2. Lactose is a reducing disaccharide. Describe how a solution of lactose would react toward these reagents.

(a) Benedict

(b) Barfoed

(c) Seliwanoff

3. What causes the Tyndall effect?

EXPERIMENT 35

Glucose Concentration in Sheep Blood

MATERIALS AND EQUIPMENT

Solutions: Sheep blood, 0.2 M zinc sulfate ($ZnSO_4 \cdot 7H_2O$), 0.2 M barium hydroxide [$Ba(OH)_2 \cdot 8H_2O$], arsenomolybdate reagent, copper reagent, 10% bleach solution, six standard glucose solutions ($C_6H_{12}O_6$) (see Table 35.1). Equipment: Marbles (~20 mm diameter), 10 mL graduated pipet, 50 mL Erlenmeyer flask, protective gloves, spectrophotometer.

 The importance of safe handling of blood and body fluids cannot be stressed enough. It should be noted that more than 20 infectious diseases can be transmitted via whole human blood or body-fluid contamination. These diseases include, but are not limited to, human immunodeficiency virus (HIV), hepatitis viruses (A, B, C, and D), cytomegalovirus, tetanus, tuberculosis, herpes simplex virus, malaria, rocky mountain spotted fever, and Creutzfeldt-Jacob disease. For any experiment in this lab manual, animal (mammalian) blood purchased from a certified supply company (or freshly drawn by a qualified technician) can be substituted. We do not have to worry about the same types of contamination and disease transmission that put us at risk with human blood. However, animal blood can become contaminated. Always assume that any blood (or other body fluid) can infect you with a disease. Safe practices will prepare you for working in a clinical environment where you may be exposed to human blood and body fluids from patients who are sick and contagious. Safe handling and disposal practices include the following:

1. Never allow blood to touch your unprotected skin. Always wear gloves and safety glasses when working with blood, even animal blood.

2. Do not put anything on the lab bench that has touched blood.

3. Any procedure that has potential for creating droplets or spills should be done very carefully. Ask your instructor if you are in doubt about how to avoid this.

4. Cleanup all blood spills and glassware with a 10% bleach solution or disinfectant prepared for this purpose. Always wear gloves during the cleanup and dispose of contaminated materials in the biohazard container provided.

DISCUSSION

Blood is a metabolic ocean of life-giving molecules and electrolytes. One of the most critical constituents of blood is glucose, a monosaccharide used by practically all organisms as (1) a source of ATP (adenosine triphosphate) and (2) as a building block of storage polymers such as glycogen (animal starch). In the adult human, normal levels of blood glucose are in the range 70-110/mg per 100 mL of whole blood. A blood glucose level higher than that range is diagnostic for diabetes and suggests there is a problem with glucose metabolism.

There are many ways to measure the concentration of glucose in blood including the clinical test strips and kits that diabetics buy in the pharmacy to monitor their blood sugar every day. This experiment demonstrates a classic colorimetric assay which uses the spectrophotometer to measure the amount of light absorbed by blood glucose which has interacted with Cu^{2+} and other reagents to form blue complexes in solution. Review Experiment 16 for background information on the spectrophotometer and the absorption spectrum of solutions.

Glucose is a reducing sugar capable of reducing Cu^{2+} to Cu^+. The Cu^+ ion is also a reducing agent which enables it to form blue complexes with arsenomolybdate reagent. The color intensity of these blue complexes in solution is proportional to the concentration of glucose that initiated the sequence of reducing reactions.

A spectrophotometer generates a beam of photons which can be set at a predetermined wavelength. The light is passed into and through a sample of a colored solution. Some of the photons will be absorbed by and some will pass through (transmitted) the sample solution. The amount absorbed depends on 1) the concentration of the colored species in solution, 2) the distance the light travels through the solution (pathlength), and 3) the wavelength of the light source (photons). In this experiment, the wavelength is preset at 495 nanometers (nm) and the pathlength is the same for all samples because the same size and optical quality cuvette (test tube) is used for every sample. Therefore, the absorption of light is determined primarily by the concentration of the glucose which influenced the intensity of the blue complexes.

The concentration of glucose in a blood sample is compared to the concentration of glucose in a set of standard glucose solutions of known concentration. The absorbance of light by these standards is used to create a calibration curve by plotting the absorbance of each sample (dependent variable) versus its concentration (independent variable). Figure 35.1 shows a sample calibration curve.

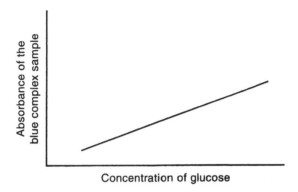

Figure 35.1 Calibration Curve for Glucose

This curve is then used to interpolate the absorbance values measured for blood glucose samples so the corresponding concentration of glucose can be determined.

Glucose is only one of many components found in blood. Since we want to measure only the concentration of the blue complexes formed by the reducing sugar glucose, other substances that interfere, such as proteins, must be removed. Otherwise, values of glucose will be obtained that are higher than the true values. A method, known as the Somogyi-Nelson procedure, is used to remove both proteins and nonsugar-reducing substances from blood.

In the Somogyi-Nelson procedure, barium hydroxide and zinc sulfate are added to precipitate both proteins and nonsugar-reducing substances. Proteins form insoluble zinc proteinates while the various reducing species are removed as either zinc or barium salts. These precipitates must be filtered or centrifuged from the mixture to obtain a clear solution for glucose analysis.

PROCEDURE

 Wear protective glasses.

Wear protective gloves.

CAUTION: Use a rubber suction bulb or water aspirator pump to draw liquids into your pipet. **Do not pipet by mouth.** The arsenomolybdate reagent contains sodium arsenate, a deadly poison. You must not mouth pipet and all solutions **must** be discarded in the arsenic waste containers. Wear protective gloves at all times.

A. Removal of Proteins and Nonsugar-reducing Substances

1. Pipet 2.0 mL of the sheep blood or an aseptic simulated blood sample into a small (50 mL) Erlenmeyer flask.

2. Using a pipet, add 14.0 mL of distilled water and mix.

3. Again, using a pipet, add 2.0 mL of 0.2 M barium hydroxide solution and mix by swirling for at least one minute.

4. Pipet 2.0 mL of 0.2 M zinc sulfate solution into the mixture in the flask. Mix thoroughly and let stand for five minutes.

5. Filter the mixture (see Figure 1.8 for the filtration set-up). Do not wet the filter paper before filtering. The blood filtrate should be a water clear solution.

 6. Handle the filter paper with forceps and discard in the biohazardous waste container provided.

B. Preparation of Samples

1. Thoroughly clean and dry nine test tubes and label them 1 to 9.

2. Fill one test tube with 24.0 mL of water and mark a line on the side to indicate this volume. Using this mark as a guide, mark all of the other tubes in a similar manner.

3. Pipet 3.0 mL of the appropriate liquid into each tube according to Table 35.1.

C. Production of Blue Complexes

1. Pipet 1.0 mL of the copper reagent into each test tube and swirl to mix.

2. Transfer all 9 test tubes (simultaneously, if possible) to a beaker containing boiling water. To prevent evaporation, place a marble on top of each test tube. Let the test tubes stand in this bath for at least 10 minutes.

Table 35.1   Material for Preparation of Samples

Tube No.	Material
1	Distilled water
2	2.0 mg/100 mL glucose standard
3	5.0 mg/100 mL glucose standard
4	8.0 mg/100 mL glucose standard
5	12.0 mg/100 mL glucose standard
6	15.0 mg 100 mL glucose standard
7	18.0 mg/100 mL glucose standard
8	Blood filtrate
9	Blood filtrate

3. Remove the marbles and place the test tubes in an ice-water bath for 5 minutes. Remove the test tubes from the ice-water bath and place them in the test tube rack.

4. Pipet 1.0 mL of the arsenomolybdate reagent into each test tube and gently mix. Let these solutions stand at room temperature for 5 minutes.

5. Dilute each solution with distilled water to the 24 mL mark. Using a rubber stopper to close the test tube, thoroughly mix the contents by repeated inversions.

D. Measurement of Absorbance for Samples and Standards

1. Plug in the spectrophotometer power line and switch the instrument on by turning the control knob clockwise past the click. Allow the instrument to warm up for 20 minutes before making any measurements. Be sure you understand the operation of the instrument before continuing. This may require a brief demonstration by the instructor.

2. Set the wavelength of your instrument to 495 nm.

3. Pour approximately 2 mL of solution from Tube 1 (distilled water) into a clean cuvette, put the cuvette into the sample holder and close the cover. Adjust the light control knob so the scale reads 0.0 Å (no absorbance). No glucose is in this first "sample" so the machine is calibrated to say that no light is absorbed. Record the absorbance on the report form.

4. Remove and empty the cuvette and thoroughly rinse with the next solution to be tested (Tube 2). Remember that tubes 1-9 contain sodium arsenate which must be handled and disposed of very carefully. Additionally, tubes 8 and 9 contained sheep blood which adds another safety concern. Pour approximately 2 mL of the standard from Tube 2 into the rinsed cuvette. Make sure the cuvette is dry on the outside. Measure the absorbance of this solution and record the data on the report form.

5. Repeat this procedure with tubes 3-9. Note: rinse the cuvette twice with the solutions in Tubes 8 and 9.

  Discard all solutions in the Arsenic/biohazard waste containers provided.

REPORT FOR EXPERIMENT 35

Glucose Concentration in Sheep Blood

Data Table

Sample No.	Absorbance	Concentration (mg glucose/100 mL)
1		0.0
2		2.0
3		5.0
4		8.0
5		12.0
6		15.0
7		18.0
8		
9		

Plot the data obtained from Samples 2 through 7 on the graph paper provided. Draw the best straight line through the data points. Read the concentration values for Samples 8 and 9, and record them in the data table.

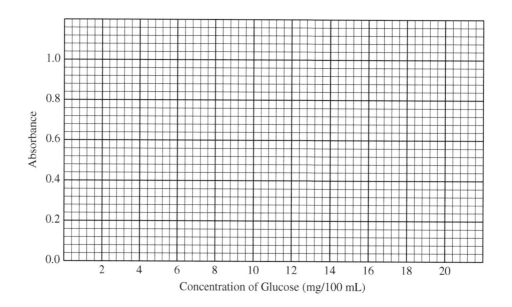

QUESTIONS AND PROBLEMS

1. Average the glucose concentration values for Samples 8 and 9. Calculate the concentration of glucose in the sheep blood. (In your calculation consider that the blood has been diluted.)

2. The concentrations you have been working with have units of mg/100 mL. Calculate the molar concentration of glucose in a blood sample containing 115 mg/100 mL.

3. Did your sheep blood glucose samples have exactly the same absorbance? List some reasons why they could vary in value.

EXPERIMENT 36

Amino Acids and Proteins

MATERIALS AND EQUIPMENT

Solids: Tyrosine [p-HOC$_6$H$_4$—CH$_2$CH(NH$_2$)COOH], urea [CO(NH$_2$)$_2$]. **Liquids:** Glacial acetic acid (HC$_2$H$_3$O$_2$), nonfat (skim) milk. **Solutions:** 10% acetic acid (HC$_2$H$_3$O$_2$), 2% albumin, 1% copper(II) sulfate (CuSO$_4$), 2% gelatin, 1% glycine (H$_2$NCH$_2$COOH), dilute (6 M) hydrochloric acid (HCl), 0.1 M lead(II) acetate [Pb(C$_2$H$_3$O$_2$)$_2$], 0.3% ninhydrin in acetone, dilute (6 M) nitric acid (HNO$_3$), concentrated nitric acid (HNO$_3$), 1-nitroso-2-naphthol (0.1% in acetone) (C$_{10}$H$_7$NO$_2$), 1% phenol (C$_6$H$_5$OH), 10% sodium hydroxide (NaOH).

DISCUSSION

Proteins are complex biomolecules present in each cell of all living organisms. They function as structural material and as enzymes, the biological catalysts which regulate the multitude of chemical reactions that maintain life. Chemically, proteins are polymers of α-amino acids joined together by bonds called **peptide linkages.**

A.   Amino Acids

All α-amino acids are carboxylic acids that include an amino (—NH$_2$) functional group attached to C-2 (the alpha carbon) and are thus called α-amino acids.

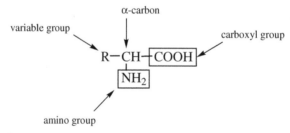

The structure also includes another group, R, which is variable depending on the amino acid. For example, when R is H— the amino acid is glycine; when R is CH3—, the amino acid is alanine (see your text for a list of the common a-amino acids and their structure).

B.   Polypeptides and Proteins

A peptide linkage in an amide structure is formed by splitting out a molecule of water between the carboxyl group of one amino acid and the amino group of another. If 40-50 amino acids are linked together the polymer is called a **polypeptide** (See Figure 36.1)

$$
\begin{array}{c}
\text{H} \quad \text{H} \;\; \text{O} \quad \text{H} \;\; \text{H} \;\; \text{O} \quad \text{H} \;\; \text{H} \;\; \text{O} \quad \text{H} \;\; \text{H} \;\; \text{O} \\
\;\;\mid\;\;\;\mid\;\;\;\parallel\;\;\;\mid\;\;\;\mid\;\;\;\parallel\;\;\;\mid\;\;\;\mid\;\;\;\parallel\;\;\;\mid\;\;\;\mid\;\;\;\parallel \\
-\text{N}-\text{C}-\text{C}-\text{N}-\text{C}-\text{C}-\text{N}-\text{C}-\text{C}-\text{N}-\text{C}-\text{C}- \\
\;\;\mid\;\;\;\;\;\;\;\;\;\;\;\mid\;\;\;\;\;\;\;\;\;\;\;\mid\;\;\;\;\;\;\;\;\;\;\;\mid \\
\text{R}_1 \qquad\quad \text{R}_2 \qquad\quad \text{R}_3 \qquad\quad \text{R}_4
\end{array}
$$

Figure 36.1   Segment of a polypeptide chain formed from α-amino acids. The R's represent the side chains (variable groups) of the amino acids and the arrows point out the peptide linkages in the polypeptide chain.

In a typical protein, hundreds—sometimes thousands—of amino acids are linked together to form the **primary structure** of a protein. In the early 1950s Frederick Sanger introduced the concept that each kind of protein has a specific amino acid sequence. He succeeded in determining the amino acid sequence of insulin and was award the Nobel Prize in 1958 for his work.

The polypeptide chains of proteins also have a **secondary structure** or configuration which occurs when the primary chains are coiled into alpha helices or arranged side-by-side as pleated sheets which are stabilized by hydrogen bonding between adjacent amino acids. The final folded shape of protein, referred to as the **tertiary structure,** is driven by the chemical nature of its R groups and how they interact with water. Finally, many tertiary level polypeptides associate together to form a functional protein known as the **quarternary structure.**

Because the amino acids in all proteins include an amino group, proteins differ from carbohydrates and fats not only in their functions in the living organism, but also in elemental composition. In addition to carbon, hydrogen, and oxygen, which are present in carbohydrates and fats, proteins contain nitrogen. Because some amino acid R groups include sulfur, sulfur is present in all proteins that include the amino acids cystine, cysteine, and methionine. Additional elements such as phosphorus, iron, copper, zinc, and iodine also occur in certain complex proteins. These elements are not part of the primary protein structure but are constituents of non-protein substances combined with proteins.

C.   Tests for Proteins and Amino Acids

Many tests have been devised to detect and distinguish among amino acids, peptides, and proteins. Characteristic colors are produced when certain reagents react with one or more of the constituent groups in a protein molecule. The color produced with a given reagent will vary in intensity with different proteins because all proteins contain different amino acids or do not contain the same amounts of a color-producing group. In this experiment, color-producing reactions will be used to obtain qualitative information about the composition of selected proteins. Various substances other than proteins or amino acids also give colors with some of the reagents. The colors produced with these substances will be compared to those produced with proteins and amino acids. The five tests included in this experiment are the Biuret Test, Tyrosine Test, Ninhydrin Test, Xanthoproteic Test and Test for cystine and cysteine sulfur in proteins.

In this experiment, these tests will be performed on three proteins, casein derived from milk, albumin, and gelatin. The same tests will be performed on nonprotein molecules including urea, phenol, and specific amino acids.

1.   Biuret Test

This test derives its name from biuret, a compound formed by heating urea to 180°C.

$$2 \; \text{H}-\overset{\overset{\displaystyle H}{|}}{N}-\overset{\overset{\displaystyle O}{||}}{C}-\overset{\overset{\displaystyle H}{|}}{N}-\text{H} \quad \xrightarrow{\;\Delta\;} \quad \text{H}-\overset{\overset{\displaystyle H}{|}}{N}-\overset{\overset{\displaystyle O}{||}}{C}-\overset{\overset{\displaystyle H}{|}}{N}-\overset{\overset{\displaystyle O}{||}}{C}-\overset{\overset{\displaystyle H}{|}}{N}-\text{H} \quad + \quad NH_3(g)$$

Urea   Biuret

The biuret test involves heating a strongly alkaline solution of the test material with a little copper(II) sulfate and is very sensitive for proteins and polypeptides containing at least three peptide units. Biuret produces a violet color, but dipeptides do not give a positive biuret test. Colors ranging from pink to blue are produced both by polypeptides and proteins containing a structure with at least two peptide linkages (indicated by the arrows), thus

$$-\overset{\overset{\displaystyle O}{||}}{C}-\overset{\overset{\displaystyle H}{|}}{N}-\overset{\overset{\displaystyle H}{|}}{\underset{\underset{\displaystyle R}{|}}{C}}-\overset{\overset{\displaystyle O}{||}}{C}-\overset{\overset{\displaystyle H}{|}}{N}-$$

2. Tyrosine Test

This test is a very sensitive method for detecting the presence of the amino acid tyrosine, either by itself or in proteins.

3. Ninhydrin Test

Alpha-amino acids react with ninhydrin (triketohydrindene hydrate) to form a blue to purple colored complex. (Proline forms a yellow color.) This reaction is the basis for identification of amino acids by chromatography and also for the quantitative colorimetric determination of amino acids present in solution. During the reaction, ammonia is liberated which reacts with ninhydrin to give the colored complex.

Ninhydrin   Colored Complex

4. Xanthoproteic Test

The xanthoproteic test (pronounced zan-tho-pro-teyic) is shown by most proteins and is due to the presence of the phenyl group, $-C_6H_5$, which reacts with nitric acid to form colored nitro compounds. (Phenylalanine generally does not give a positive test.)

5. Test for Cystine and Cysteine Sulfur in Proteins

When proteins containing cysteine are heated with a NaOH solution, the sulfur is converted into sulfide ions (S^{2-}). (Methionine usually does not react.) The presence of sulfide ion in solution is detected by reacting with lead(II) acetate to form a black precipitate of lead(II)sulfide.

D. Proteins as a Food Source: Milk

Proteins are one of the three major classes of foods (proteins, carbohydrates, and fats). Nutritionally, milk is an almost complete food containing proteins, fats, carbohydrates, many minerals, and a number of important vitamins. The proteins include casein, lactalbumin, and lactoglobin. Casein makes up about 80% of the protein in cow's milk and about 40% of that in human milk. The casein in milk is a phosphoprotein containing about 0.7% phosphorus. It is present as calcium caseinate in cows milk and as potassium caseinate in human milk.

Casein is released from its salts and precipitated from nonfat milk by treating with dilute acetic or hydrochloric acids. However, care must be taken not to use too much acid because free casein acts as a base and redissolves in excess acid. In addition to being a food, casein is used industrially in the manufacture of adhesives, paints, paper coatings, and in printing textiles and wallpaper.

PROCEDURE

 Wear protective glasses.

Dispose of all solids and liquids in the containers provided.

A. Separation and Testing of Casein

1. Separation of Casein: Mix 50 mL of nonfat milk with 50 mL of water in a 250 mL beaker. Add 10% acetic acid dropwise from a pipet or a medicine dropper, with vigorous stirring, until a flocculent precipitate forms. From 2 to 3 mL of the acetic acid is usually required. Avoid excess acid. Allow the precipitated casein to settle for a few minutes. Decant the supernant liquid through filter paper in a funnel. Then pour all of the precipitate into the funnel. Finally remove excess moisture from the casein by pressing the precipitate between absorbent paper.

The filtration process may take some time to complete, therefore, you should do all the other tests while the liquid drains from the funnel and then complete the experiment with casein.

2. Tests on Casein: For each of the following tests, mix a quantity of casein about the size of a small pea with the appropriate amount of water (3–5 mL). Perform the test and record whether the result is positive or negative.

(a) Biuret   (c) Ninhydrin

(b) Tyrosine   (d) Xanthoproteic

B. Biuret Test

1. Place 0.6 gram of urea in a dry test tube and carefully heat over a Bunsen flame. After the urea has melted, continue heating for about 30 seconds. Stop heating, and immediately note the odor (CAUTION) of the gas being emitted. Allow the tube to cool, add about 8 mL of water, and mix to dissolve some of the residue. Set aside for the Biuret test procedure.

Biuret Test Procedure: To a clean test tube add 4 mL of the solution to be tested, 1.0 mL 10% NaOH solution, and 4 drops 1% $CuSO_4$ solution. Mix and note the color that develops.

2. Do biuret tests on these solutions. Record your observations in the data table.

(a) Solution derived from heating urea in Part B1.

(b) 2% albumin

(c) 1% glycine

(d) Water (blank)

C. Tyrosine Test

Tyrosine Test Procedure: To a clean test tube add 0.5 to 1.0 mL of the solution to be tested and 2 drops of 0.1% 1-nitroso-2-naphthol (in acetone) and mix. At this stage of the tyrosine test, each tested solution should be a very light yellow. Add 3 drops dilute (6 M) HNO_3 and mix. Heat each tube in boiling water for approximately 1 minute. Note the color that develops (a positive tyrosine test will give a pink to red color for the heated solution).

Do the Tyrosine test on these solutions. Record your observations.

(a) 2% albumin

(b) 1% phenol

(c) 1% glycine

(d) 5 mL water to which a very small amount of tyrosine has been added (from the tip of a spatula)

(e) 2% gelatin

(f) Water (blank)

D. Ninhydrin Test

Ninhydrin Test Procedure: To a clean test tube add 5 mL of the solution to be tested and 10 drops of ninhydrin solution. Mix and heat the mixture in a boiling water bath for about 2 minutes. Note the color that develops.

Do the ninhydrin test on these solutions. Record your observations.

(a) 2% albumin

(b) 1% glycine

(c) 1% phenol

(d) Water (blank)

E. Xanthoproteic Test

Xanthoproteic Test Procedure: To a clean test tube add 3 mL of the solution to be tested and 10 drops of concentrated nitric acid. Mix and note any changes. Heat the tube 3 to 4 minutes in a beaker of boiling water and note any color changes. Cool and add 1% NaOH solution (3–4 mL) until the solution is alkaline (test with red litmus). Note the color change.

Do the xanthoproteic test on the following solutions. Record your observations.

(a) 2% albumin

(b) 1% glycine

(c) 1% phenol

(d) 2% gelatin

(e) Water (blank)

F. Test for Cysteine Sulfur in Proteins

Test Procedure: To a clean test tube add 3 mL of the solution to be tested and 2 mL of 10% NaOH solution. Heat the tube in a boiling water bath for 1 to 2 minutes. Remove the tube from the water bath and add 4 drops of lead(II) acetate solution and note the results. Add dilute (6 M) HCl (2 to 3 mL) with slight warming until the dark color disappears. Carefully smell and note the odor of the solution.

Do the sulfur test on these solutions.

(a) 2% albumin

(b) 2% gelatin

(c) Water (blank)

REPORT FOR EXPERIMENT 36

Amino Acids and Proteins

A. Separation and Testing of Casein from Milk

Use (+) and (−) signs to indicate whether each test on casein was positive or negative.

Biuret	Tyrosine	Ninhydrin	Xanthoproteic

B. Biuret Test

Data Table

Solution	Color observation
(a) Heated urea	
(b) 2% albumin	
(c) 1% glycine	
(d) Water (blank)	

1. What is the odor of the gas emitted by heated urea?

   _____

2. How could you test for this gas other than by smelling it?

3. What is the evidence for a positive biuret test?

4. Write the formula of the organic substance responsible for the color reaction noted in tube (a).

5. Does albumin give a positive biuret test?

                                              _____

6. Does glycine give a positive biuret test?

                                              _____

7. Write the structure that must be present in a protein for a positive biuret test.

C. Tyrosine Test

Data Table

Solution	Color observation
(a) albumin	
(b) 1% phenol	
(c) 1% glycine	
(d) Water + tyrosine	
(e) 2% gelatin	
(f) Water (blank)	

1. What is the evidence for a positive tyrosine test?

                                              _____

2. Write the structural formula of the amino acid that will give a positive tyrosine test.

3. Which of the proteins tested contains this/these amino acids?

                                              _____

4. Write the structural formula for a tripeptide that will give a positive tyrosine test.

D. **Ninhydrin Test**

Data Table

Solution	Observations
(a) 2% albumin	
(b) 1% glycine	
(c) 1% phenol	
(d) Water (blank)	

1. What is the evidence for a positive ninhydrin test?

2. What groups in the amino acid or protein are responsible for a positive ninhydrin test?

3. Write the name and structural formula of an amino acid (among those listed in your text) that will not give a positive ninhydrin test.

_____

4. Is it likely that there are proteins that will not give a positive ninhydrin test? Explain your answer.

E. **Xanthoproteic Test**

Data Table

Solution	Observations		
	After adding HNO_3	After heating	After adding NaOH
(a) 2% albumin			
(b) 1% glycine			
(c) 1% phenol			
(d) 2% gelatin			
(e) Water (blank)			

1. Which amino acids may be present in a protein showing a positive xanthoproteic test?

2. Why is the skin stained yellow when it comes in contact with nitric acid?

F.   Test for Cysteine Sulfur in Proteins

Data Table

Solutions	Observations	
	After adding lead(II) acetate	After adding hydrochloric acid
(a) 2% albumin		
(b) 2% gelatin		
(c) Water (blank)		

1. What is the evidence that sulfur is present?

2. Write the formula(s) of the amino acid(s) that may be present in a protein showing a positive sulfur test.

3. What is the dark colored substance that is formed when lead(II) acetate is added to the test solution? Write the equation for its formation.

4. What is the compound that you can smell after HCl is added to the dark-colored test mixture? Write the equation for its formation.

EXPERIMENT 41

Lipids

MATERIALS AND EQUIPMENT

Solids: Cholesterol ($C_{27}H_{45}OH$), potassium bisulfate ($KHSO_4$), stearic acid [$CH_3(CH_2)_{16}COOH$], vegetable shortening (Spry, Crisco, etc.). **Liquids:** Acetic anhydride [$(CH_3CO)_2O$], chloroform ($CHCl_3$), glycerol ($CH_2(OH)CH(OH)CH_2OH$), hexane (C_6H_{14}), oleic acid [$CH_3(CH_2)_7CH{=}CH(CH_2)_7COOH$], concentrated sulfuric acid (H_2SO_4), vegetable oils (cottonseed, peanut, corn, soybean, etc.). **Solutions:** 5% bromine (Br_2) in 1,1,1-trichloroethane (CCl_3CH_3), 10% sodium hydroxide (NaOH).

DISCUSSION

Lipids are naturally occurring substances that are arbitrarily grouped together on the basis of their solubility in fat solvents, such as ether, benzene, chloroform, and carbon tetrachloride, and their insolubility in water. Lipids are subdivided into classes based on structural similarities. Two important classes are the simple lipids and the steroids.

Simple Lipids. (a) Fats and oils: esters of fatty acids and glycerol. (b) Waxes: esters of high molar mass fatty acids and high molar mass alcohols.

Steroids. These are substances possessing a 17-carbon unit structure containing four fused rings known as the steroid nucleus. Cholesterol and several hormones are in this class. Steroids having an —OH (alcohol) group attached to the ring are known as sterols. Cholesterol is an example of such a substance.

Fats (and oils) are one of the three general classes of foodstuffs—carbohydrates, proteins, and fats. The distinction between a fat and an oil is that a fat is a solid at room temperature while an oil is a liquid. Both have similar molecular structure. It is a triester (triacylglycerol) that may be considered as being derived from a glycerol molecule and three fatty acid molecules; thus

In this generalized formula, the part derived from glycerol is at the left, and the ester linkages are marked by small arrows. The portions to the right of the arrows are derived from three fatty acids. The fatty acids usually contain even numbers of carbon atoms ranging from 4 to 20 or more. The number of carbon-carbon double bonds in the carbon chains (represented by R_1, R_2, or R_3 or in the generalized formula) usually varies from 0 to 4. Oleic acid, an 18-carbon acid with one double bond, is the most common unsaturated fatty acid.

A fat with no carbon-carbon double bonds is saturated. If carbon-carbon double bonds are present, the fat is unsaturated. The term polyunsaturated means that the molecules of a particular product each contain several double bonds.

Halogens add readily to carbon-carbon double bonds.

$$X_2 + -CH{=}CH- \longrightarrow -CHX-CHX-$$

A solution of bromine in 1,1,1-trichloroethane is used to detect and estimate the degree of unsaturation in fats. The reddish-brown color disappears when bromine adds to double bonds.

Fats are saponified when heated with a strong base, such as sodium hydroxide, yielding sodium salts of fatty acids (soaps) and glycerol. Fats are hydrolyzed to fatty acids and glycerol in the presence of fat splitting enzymes (lipases) or when heated with a strong acid.

Saponification: Fat + Sodium hydroxide $\xrightarrow{\Delta}$ Sodium salts of fatty acids + Glycerol
(Soaps)

Hydrolysis: Fat + Water $\xrightarrow{\text{Enzymes or } H^+}$ Fatty acids + Glycerol

Potassium bisulfate ($KHSO_4$) is used to distinguish glycerol esters from other lipids. It is both a strong acid and a powerful dehydrating agent. When $KHSO_4$ is heated with a fat, hydrolysis occurs and the glycerol produced is dehydrated to acrolein. Acrolein ($CH_2{=}CHCHO$) is an unsaturated aldehyde with a characteristic irritating odor.

Steroids are widely distributed in plants and animals and have a variety of functions. Examples of steroids are cholesterol, the sex hormones, ergosterol (which is a precursor of vitamin D), bile salts (which aid in the digestion of fats) and cortisone and prednisone (potent steroid hormones useful in the treatment of inflamation). Steroids have a 17-carbon skeletal structure consisting of four fused rings, numbered as shown.

This hydrocarbon skeleton may have varying amounts of unsaturation and be substituted at various points, especially at positions 3 and 17.

Cholesterol is the most abundant steroid in the body and occurs in foods from animal sources such as eggs, butter, meat, and cheese. Cholesterol is not found in plant tissues, but closely related steroids are present in plants.

Minute amounts of cholesterol and related steroids can be detected by the Lieberman-Burchard test. This test involves treating a chloroform solution of the steroid with acetic anhydride and concentrated sulfuric acid. The formation of a blue-green color is a positive test.

PROCEDURE

 Wear protective glasses.

NOTES:

1. Clean, dry test tubes are needed in this experiment and may be prepared as follows:

    (a) Clean each tube by brushing with hot water containing detergent.

    (b) Rinse thoroughly with water. For spotless tubes, rinse once with distilled water.

    (c) Wipe the outside of the tube, shake out excess water, grasp the tube with a test tube holder and heat over a nonluminous burner flame (without an inner cone) until dry.

    (d) Allow the tube to cool.

2. The tubes containing the reaction mixture from the acrolein test should be filled with hot water and allowed to soak for several minutes before cleaning by the method given in Note 1, above.

 Dispose of all substances in the container provided.

A. Acrolein Test

Place about 0.4 g (no more than 0.5 g) potassium bisulfate in a clean, dry test tube. Add 2 drops (or 0.05 to 0.1 g) of the material to be tested, and make sure that it is in contact with the potassium bisulfate. Now, using a test tube holder, heat the bottom of the tube over a hot burner flame. Incline the mouth of the tube at an angle of about 45° and constantly agitate the mixture by shaking the tube while heating, moving it in and out of the flame to control the rate of heating.

 CAUTION: Keep the mouth of the tube pointed away from yourself and away from others while it is being heated; there is danger of spattering, and hot potassium bisulfate is an extremely disagreeable substance.

Continue heating until the potassium bisulfate is melted and a very slight darkening of the tube contents is visible. Stop heating and cautiously note the odor of the vapor coming from the tube by fanning it toward your nose from a distance of 3 to 6 inches. Acrolein produces a characteristic sharp irritating odor.

Do the acrolein test on the following materials in the order given. Describe and record qualitative differences, as well as intensity differences, among the odors produced.

1. Vegetable oil (cottonseed, corn, peanut, or safflower)

2. Oleic acid (or stearic acid)

3. Glycerol

B.   Reaction with Bromine

Place 7 clean, dry test tubes in a rack, and add 3 mL of hexane to each. Hexane is used here as a solvent. Add the following substances to the hexane in the test tubes.

Tube No.	Material
1	Nothing (Control)
2	3 drops vegetable oil (Peanut, cottonseed, or corn)
3	3 drops of glycerol
4	0.1 g stearic acid
5	3 drops oleic acid
6	0.1 g cholesterol
7	3 drops melted vegetable shortening

Mix the contents of each tube thoroughly for several seconds by firmly holding the top with one hand and tapping the side of the tube near the bottom with the forefinger of the other hand. **Do the following in the hood.** Add 2 drops of 5% bromine in 1,1,1-trichloroethane to Tube 1. Mix and note whether the bromine color has faded at 10 seconds and at 30 seconds following the bromine addition. Record your observations on the Report Sheet using this code: 0 = No fading, or barely noticeable fading, of color. 1 = Definitely noticeable color fading, but not complete. 2 = Complete, or nearly complete, disappearance of color.

Repeat the addition of bromine and the 10 and 30 second observations for each of the 6 remaining tubes in succession, and record your observations on the Report Sheet.

 Dispose of liquids in the waste organic solvent bottle.

C.   Lieberman-Burchard Test

Place 5 clean, dry test tubes in a rack and add the materials to be tested as follows:

Tube No.	Material
1	Stearic acid, pinhead sized quantity
2	Cholesterol, pinhead sized quantity
3	Glycerol, 2 drops
4	Vegetable oil, 2 drops (Cottonseed, peanut, soybean, or corn)
5	Melted vegetable shortening, 2 drops

Do the following in the hood. Add 2 mL chloroform, 10 drops acetic anhydride, and 2 drops concentrated sulfuric acid to each tube, and mix thoroughly. After 5 minutes note the color present and its relative intensity in each solution. Record your data on the Report Form.

This is a sensitive test for the presence of steroids. Colors changing from pinkish, to blue, to green develop in the course of the reaction. The intensity of the color is roughly proportional to the amount of steroid present.

 Dispose of liquids in the waste organic solvent bottle.

D. Saponification

Put 4 drops of vegetable oil or melted shortening into a test tube, and add 10 drops of 10% NaOH solution. Now using a test tube holder, incline the tube at an angle of about 45° and heat the contents over a low burner flame.

 CAUTION: Be sure to wear your safety glasses and keep the tube pointed away from others, and from yourself, while it is being heated.

Shake the tube constantly while heating so that the liquid is continually sloshed about in the bottom third of the tube. Control the rate of heating by moving the tube in and out of the flame. Continue heating with constant agitation until the mixture in the tube is almost dry or until a solid begins to form. Allow the tube to cool for at least 2 minutes; add 5 mL of distilled water, stopper, and shake the tube vigorously for several seconds. Note and record the results.

To another test tube, add 4 drops of the vegetable oil and 10 drops of 10% NaOH solution. Do not heat this tube, but add 5 mL distilled water; stopper, and shake the tube vigorously for several seconds. Compare the results with those obtained with the first tube.

 Dispose of residue down the sink drain.

REPORT FOR EXPERIMENT 41

Lipids

A. Acrolein Test

1. Describe the odors produced by (a) vegetable oil, (b) oleic acid (or stearic acid), and (c) glycerol.

2. Which substance(s) gave a positive acrolein test?

B. Reaction with Bromine

Tube No.	Material tested	Color 10 sec. (0,1, or 2)	Color 30 sec. (0,1, or 2)	Conclusions (Saturated or unsaturated)
1				
2				
3				
4				
5				
6				
7				

C. Lieberman-Burchard Test

Tube No.	Material tested	Color and relative intensity	Conclusions Positive or negative
1			
2			
3			
4			
5			

D. Saponification

Observations in:

First test tube:

Second test tube:

QUESTIONS AND PROBLEMS

1. Write the structural formula of a triacylglycerol molecule that is made from glycerol and three molecules of stearic acid. Draw a box around the portion(s) of the molecule that make it soluble in solvents such as benzene or hexane.

2. Glycerol is a saturated trihydroxy alcohol. Acrolein is an unsaturated aldehyde having the formula, $CH_2=CHCHO$. Hot potassium bisulfate is a powerful dehydrating agent. Using structural formulas for organic substances, write an equation to show how hot $KHSO_4$ converts glycerol to acrolein.

3. Explain why the fat, glyceryl tripalmitate, and cholesterol would be expected to give different results with the Acrolein Test.

4. Write an equation showing the addition of bromine to oleic acid.

5. Does the vegetable oil (or oils) tested contain substances other than glycerides? Cite experimental results which justify your answer.

6. What was the evidence in Part D that the vegetable oil was saponified?

7. Write condensed structural formulas and names for the soaps produced in Part D if vegetable oil contained glycerides of lauric, palmitic, and oleic acids.

STUDY AID I

Significant Figures

Every measurement that we make has some inherent error due to the limitations of the measuring instrument and the experimenter. The numerical value recorded for a measurement should give some indication of the reliability (precision) of that measurement. In measuring a temperature using a thermometer calibrated at one-degree intervals we can easily read the thermometer to the nearest one degree, but we normally estimate and record the temperature to the nearest tenth of a degree (0.1°C). For example, a temperature falling between 23°C and 24°C might be estimated at 23.4°C. There is some uncertainly about the last digit, 4, but an estimate of it is better information than simply reporting 23°C or 24°C. If we read the thermometer as "exactly" twenty-three degrees, the temperature should be reported as 23.0°C, not 23°C, because 23.0°C indicates our estimate to the nearest 0.1°C. Thus in recording any measurement, we retain one uncertain digit. The digits retained in a physical measurement are said to be significant, and are called **significant figures.**

Some numbers are exact (have no uncertain digits) and therefore have an infinite number of significant figures. Exact numbers occur in simple counting operations, such as 5 bricks, and in defined relationships, such as 100 cm = 1 meter, 24 hours = 1 day, etc. Because of their infinite number of significant figures, exact numbers do not limit or determine the number of significant figures in a calculation.

Counting Significant Figures. Digits other than zero are always significant. Depending on their position in the number, zeros may or may not be significant. There are several possible situations:

1. All zeros between other digits in a number are significant; for example: 3.076, 4002, 790.2. Each of these numbers has four significant figures.

2. Zeros to the left of the first nonzero digit are used to locate the decimal point and are not significant. Thus 0.013 has only two significant figures (1 and 3); The zero is not significant.

3. Zeros to the right of the last nonzero digit, and to the right of the decimal point are significant, for they would not have been included except to express precision. For example, 3.070 has four significant figures; 0.070 has two significant figures.

4. Zeros to the right of the last nonzero digit, but to the left of the decimal, as in the numbers 100, 580, 37000, etc., may not be significant. For example, in 37000 the measurement might be good to the nearest 1000, 100, 10, or 1. There are two conventions which may be used to show the intended precision. If all the zeros are significant, then an expressed decimal may be added, as 580., or 37000. But a better system, and one which is applicable to the case when some but not all of the zeros are significant, is to express the number in exponential notation, including only the significant zeros. Thus for 300, if the zero following 3 is significant, we would write 3.0×10^2. For 17000, if two zeros are significant, we would write 1.700×10^4. The number we correctly expressed as 580. can also be expressed as 5.80×10^2. With exponential notation there is no doubt as to the number of significant figures.

Addition or Subtraction. The result of an addition or subtraction should contain no more digits to the right of the decimal point than are in that quantity which has the least number of digits to the right of the decimal point. Perform the operation indicated and then round off the number to the proper significant figure.

Example:

$$
\begin{array}{r}
24.372 \\
72.21 \\
6.1488 \\
\hline
102.7308 \ (102.73)
\end{array}
$$

Since the digit 1 in 72.21 is uncertain, the sum can have no digits beyond this point, so the sum should be rounded off to 102.73.

Multiplication or Division. In multiplication or division, the answer can have no more significant figures than the factor with the least number of significant figures. In multiplication or division, the position of the decimal point has nothing to do with the number of significant figures in the answer.

Example: $3.1416 \times 7.5 \times 252 = 5937.624(5.9 \times 10^3)$

The operations of arithmetic supply all the digits shown, but this does not make the answer precise to seven significant figures. Most of these digits are not realistic because of the limited precision of the number 7.5. So the answer must be rounded to two significant figures, 5900 or 5.9×10^3. It should be emphasized that in rounding-off the number you are not sacrificing precision, since the digits discarded are not really meaningful.

Example: $\dfrac{(27.52)(62.5)}{1.22} = 1409.836(1.41 \times 10^3)$

The answer should contain three (3) significant figures.

STUDY AID 3

Preparing and Reading A Graph

A graph is often the most convenient way to present or display a set of data. Various kinds of graphs have been devised, but the most common type uses a set of horizontal and vertical coordinates, x and y, to show the relationship between two variables, the independent and dependent variables. The dependent variable is a measurement that changes as a result of changes in the independent variable. The independent variable either changes itself (like time) or is controlled by the experimenter. Usually the independent variable is plotted on the x-axis (abscissa) and the dependent variable is plotted on the y-axis (ordinate). See Figure S3.1.

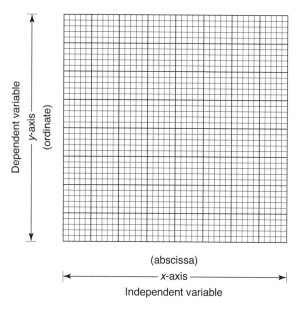

Figure S3.1   Rectangular coordinate graph paper

The values for each variable are called data and listed in a data table to facilitate the construction of a graph. As a specific example of how a graph is constructed, let us graph the relationship between the volume of a liquid and its mass. A chemist measured increasing volumes of a liquid and determined the mass of each volume. The data are recorded in Table S3.1. In this study aid, we will use this data to illustrate the steps for making graphs by hand (Part A) and by computer (Part C).

A. STEPS IN PREPARING A GRAPH

Most scientists today use computers to help them make graphs from their data. Before we show you how to work with a computer to do this, it is important to learn how to make a graph with pencil, ruler, and graph paper. Use the following step-by-step procedure to plot the data in Table S3.1 on the graph paper provided in Figure S3.2. Your completed graph should resemble the graph in Figure S3.3 very closely. After you complete this first graph, practice your graphing skills by making another graph using the data in Table S3.2 and the grid provided in Figure S3.4.

PROCEDURE

1. Examine the graph paper in Figure S3.2 and count how many blocks are available along each axis: This paper has 40 blocks along the x-axis and 40 blocks along the y-axis.

Table S3.1   Volume vs. Mass Data

Volume, mL	Mass, g
21.0	19.1
30.0	27.3
37.5	34.1
44.0	40.0
47.0	42.8
50.0	45.5

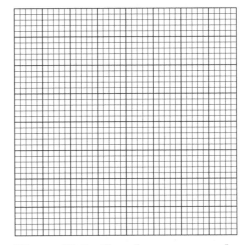

Figure S3.2   Graph paper sample

2. Examine the data in Table S3.1 and determine the independent and dependent variables: The amount of liquid in each sample was varied by the experimenter, so volume is the independent variable and will be plotted along the x-axis. The mass of each sample changed as the volume was changed, so mass is the dependent variable and will be plotted along the y-axis. Usually the independent-versus-dependent-variable decision can be reasoned out like this example. If not, then the placement of the variables on the axes can be arbitrary.

3. Determine the range for each variable: The independent variable ranges from 21.0 mL to 50.0 mL. This is a range of 29.0 mL. The dependent variable ranges from 19.1 g to 45.5 g. This is a range of 26.4 g.

4. Determine the scale for each axis; that is, how many units each block will represent. The calculation for the independent variable using this particular piece of graph paper is:

independent variable scale = 29.0 mL/40 blocks = 0.73 mL/block

But, if we adopted this scale, the graph would be extremely awkward to plot and read. So, we round **up** (never round down) this preliminary scale to a more convenient value per block. The most convenient scales to use are generally 0.5, 1, 2, 5, or 10 units per block. The scale is never rounded up to more than double its preliminary value. For this sample data, 0.73 mL/block is rounded up to 1.0 mL/block because it is convenient and less than 1.46 (double 0.73).

Now, we do the same calculations for the dependent variable on the y-axis.

dependent variable scale = 26.4 g/40 blocks = 0.66 g/block. It is not very convenient to count by units of 0.66, so this value is rounded **up** to 1.0 g per block.

5. Determine the starting values for each coordinate: Although it is common for the axes to be numbered starting with zero at the origin (lower left corner), it is not required and

sometimes it is a poor choice. For instance, in our example, all of the data for the independent variable are greater than 20.0, so from 0–20, there would be no data plotted. Therefore, we start numbering the x-axis at 20.0 mL and the y-axis at 15.0 g.

6. Determine the major and minor increments for each axis: We never number every block. Instead we number in major increments of several blocks with minor, unnumbered increments (blocks) in between. Because of our choice of scales, we will label both the x-axis and the y-axis every 5 blocks. The axes do not have to be numbered every 5 divisions, but often the graph paper has darker lines every five blocks and it is convenient to number at these heavier lines. The numbered increments must be on lines.

7. Label each axis so it is clear what each one represents: In our example, we label the x-axis as Volume, mL, and the y-axis as Mass, g. Labels and units on the coordinates are absolutely essential.

8. Plot the data points: Here is how a point is located on the graph: Using the 44.0 mL and 40.0 g data as an example, trace a vertical line up from 44.0 mL on the x-axis and a horizontal line across from 40.0 g on the y-axis and mark the point where the two lines intersect. This process is called plotting. The remaining five points are plotted on the graph in the same way. It is often helpful if each data point is neatly circled so it will be more visible. Then, if more than one set of data is plotted on the same graph, another symbol (an open triangle or square, for example) can be used.

9. Draw a smooth line through the plotted points: In our example, if the six points have been plotted correctly, they lie on a straight line so that a straight edge can be used to draw the smooth line connecting the six points. When plotting data collected in the laboratory, the best smooth line will not necessarily touch each of the plotted points. Thus, some judgment must be exercised in locating the best smooth line, whether it be straight or curved.

10. Title the graph: Every graph should have a title that clearly expresses what the graph represents. Titles may be placed above the graph or on the upper part of the graph. The latter choice, which is illustrated in Figure S3.3, is the most common for student laboratory reports. Of course, the title must be placed so as not to interfere with the plot on the graph. A completed graph of the data in Table S3.1 is shown in Figure S3.3.

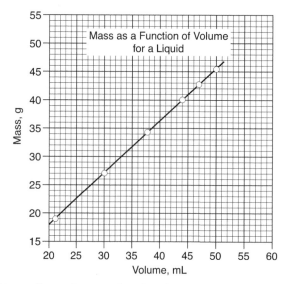

Figure S3.3 Sample graph of volume vs. mass in Table S3.1

Practice Plotting: Sample Data

Table S3.2 is a set of data for you to practice plotting a graph with the steps just described. Use the graph paper in Figure S3.4. Plot °C on the *x*-axis and °F on the *y*-axis.

Table S3.2
Temperature Scales

Temperature, °C	Temperature, °F
0	32
20	68
37	98.6
50	122
100	212

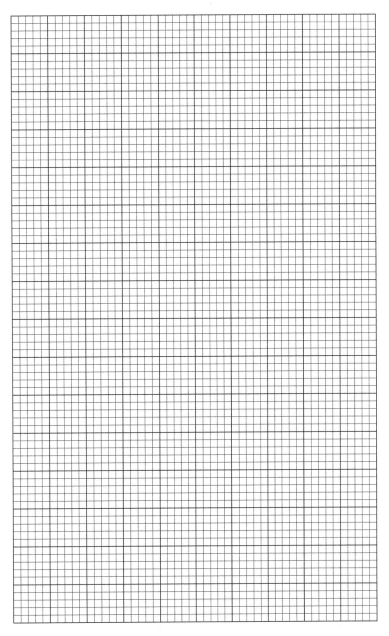

Figure S3.4   Grid for practice plotting of Table S3.2 temperature data

B.   READING A GRAPH

Although graphs are prepared from a limited number of data points (the graph in Figure S3.5 was prepared from six data points), it is possible to extract reliable data for points between the experimental data points and to infer information beyond the range of the plotted data. These skills require that you understand how to read a graph.

Table S3.3

Temperature °C	Solubility, g KClO₃/100 g water
10	5.0
20	7.4
30	10.5
50	19.3
60	24.5
80	38.5

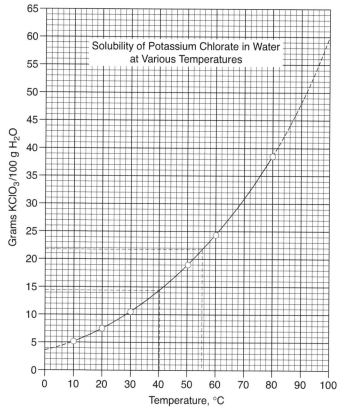

Figure S3.5 Solubility vs. temperature data from Table S3.3

Figure S3.5 is a graph showing the solubility of potassium chlorate in water at various temperatures. The solubility curve on this graph was plotted from experimentally determined solubilities at six temperatures shown in Table S3.3.

These experimentally determined solubilities are all located on the smooth curve traced by the solid line portion of the graph. We are therefore confident that the solid line represents a very good approximation of the solubility data for potassium chlorate covering the temperature range from 10°C to 80°C. All points on the plotted curve represent the composition of saturated solutions. Any point below the curve represents an unsaturated solution.

The dashed line portions of the curve are **extrapolations;** that is, they extend the curve above and below the temperature range actually covered by the plotted data. Curves such as this are often extrapolated a short distance beyond the range of the known data although the extrapolated portions may not be highly accurate. Extrapolation is justified only in the absence of more reliable information.

The graph in Figure S3.5 can be used with confidence to obtain the solubility of KClO₃ at any temperature between 10°C and 80°C but the solubilities between 0°C and 10°C and between 80°C and 100°C are less reliable. For example, what is the solubility of KClO₃ at 40°C, at 55°C, and at 100°C? First, draw a vertical line from each temperature to the plotted solubility curve. Now from each of these points on the curve, draw a horizontal line to the solubility axis and read the corresponding solubility. The values that we read from the graph are

40°C	14.6 g KClO₃/100 g water
55°C	21.9 g KClO₃/100 g water
100°C	59.8 g KClO₃/100 g water

Of these solubilities, the one corresponding to 55°C is probably the most reliable because experimental points are plotted at 50°C and 60°C. The 40°C solubility value is probably a bit less reliable because the nearest plotted points are at 30°C and 50°C. The 100°C solubility is the least reliable of the three values because it was taken from the extrapolated part of the curve, and the nearest plotted point is 80°C. Actual handbook solubility values are 14.0 g and 57.0 g of $KClO_3$/100 g water at 40°C and 100°C respectively.

Although making and reading graphs by hand in this way gets easier with practice, most scientists now use computers to graph their experimental data. If you have access to a computer either in the laboratory, library, or at home, we encourage you to learn computer graphing after you have mastered all the skills of graphing data by hand. Instructions for computer graphing are provided in Part C of this study aid.

Requirements for Computer Graphing

There are several software programs that can be used to generate graphs of scientific data. We have chosen **Microsoft Excel,** a program within *Microsoft Office 2007* (earlier versions will also work) which requires PC Windows XP or Vista. You should be sitting in front of a PC computer with Microsoft Excel 2007 active as you begin these instructions. These instructions assume that you have some knowledge of Microsoft Excel and that you know how to write graphs manually as instructed in Part A of this Study Aid. Unless you are comfortable with your computer and have used this software, there should be someone around who can help you out occasionally when you try this the first time.

C. COMPUTER GRAPHING

Preparing a computer graph involves the same steps as the paper and pencil graph. The difference is that the computer will do most of the steps for you. However, you must provide the computer with the necessary information (data) that is being graphed. After you complete all the instructions in this section, you should have a graph that looks like Figure **S3.6** below.

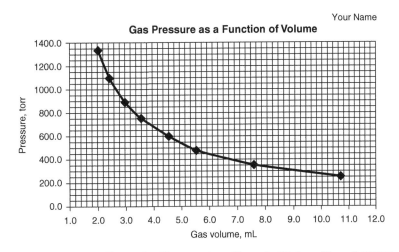

Figure S3.6   Sample Computer Graph Using Excel 2007

1. Open up a clean page (called an Excel "sheet") on which to begin the graph (called a "chart")

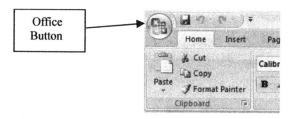

Figure S3.7

To do this, click on the office button in the upper left corner of the Excel ribbon (**Figure S3.7**). When you click on the Office Button you will open a list of functions (Figure S3.8). Click on the **New** icon and an Excell sheet as shown in Figure S3.9 will open.

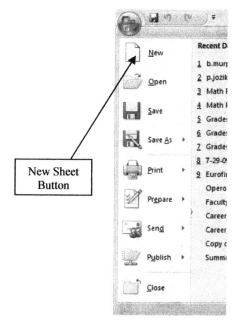

Figure S3.8

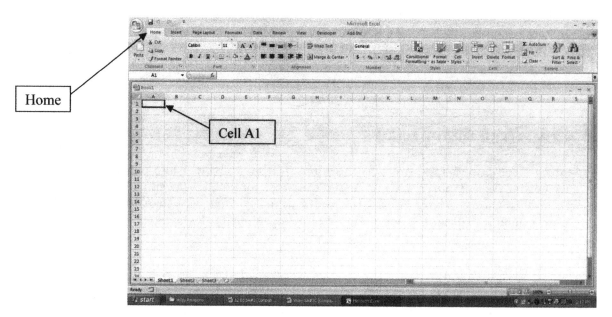

Figure S3.9   Excel Sheet with ribbon in Home open

2. Add the data table to the sheet so the graphing of the data can begin. The data graphed for this exercise is the same data that was graphed in Exercise 9, B2.

Volume, mL	10.70	7.64	5.57	4.56	3.52	2.97	2.43	2.01
Pressure, torr	250	350	480	600	760	900	1100	1330

Go to Column A on the new Excel sheet that was opened. In cell A1, type **Volume, mL** and in B1, type **Pressure, torr.** Then, enter the volume and pressure values in the columns from the data shown above. Highlight the cells that are filled in with the data. When this is done, the left side of your screen should look like **Figure S3.10**.

3. Convert the data table into a "chart" by choosing **insert** from the ribbon (**Figure S3.11**). This should immediately result in the appearance of the tool bar shown in S3.11. Click on Scatter and the menu of charts derived from this category will appear as shown below. For this set of volume and pressure data which is made up of separate measurements, select ⟶ and a graph of the volume vs. pressure data in Figure S3.10 will appear on the sheet (Figure S3.12) below.

Anytime you want to modify the chart, you must select the chart by clicking on a blank area of the chart. The border around the graph will appear (as shown in Figure S3.12). This will activate the Chart ribbon with the tools to modify the chart.

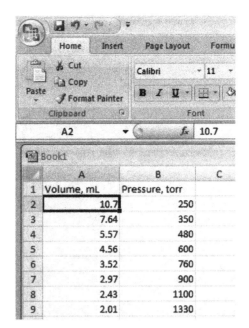

Figure S3.10   Data to be graphed

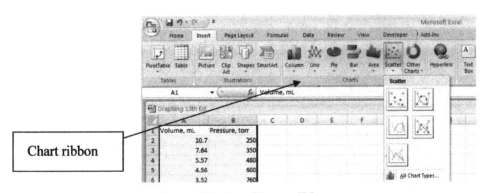

Figure S3.11   Chart ribbon

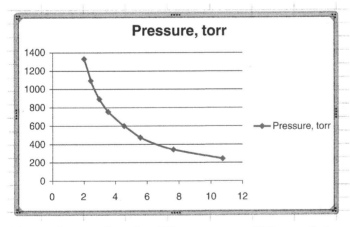

Figure S3.12   Graph of Pressure vs. Volume data before formatting

4. **Adding a Chart Title and Axis Titles.** The remaining steps in this procedure will explain how to convert this very primitive graph into the finished graph at the beginning

of the Computer Graphing instructions (**Figure S3.6**). Make sure the Chart ribbon is open, and select Chart Tools as shown below.

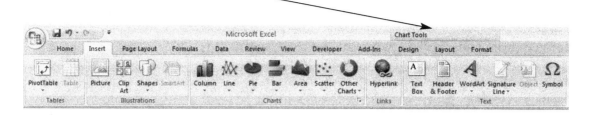

Select Layout from the Chart Tools options and a chart layout ribbon will appear as shown in Figure S3.13

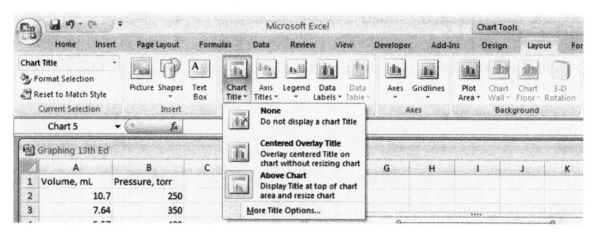

Figure S3.13

The Chart ribbon shown above will be used to complete the formatting of the graph. Choose Chart Title and the menu will appear as shown in S3.13. Click on Above Chart as shown and a text box will appear on the chart. Fill in an appropriate title for the chart: **Gas Pressure as a Function of Volume**.

5. **Adding Titles for the X and Y axes**. Select Axis Titles from the Chart Layout ribbon. From the drop down menus, select Primary Horizontal Axis Title (ie. X axis) and Title Below Axis.

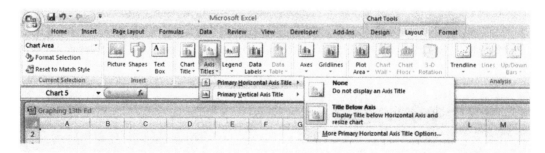

Figure S3.14

6. This will bring up a text box for adding the X-axis title: **Gas volume, mL**. Next, select Primary vertical Axis title and select **Rotated title**: rotated axis title and resize chart. This will open up a text box for adding the Y-axis title: **Pressure, torr**.

7. **Format Legend.** A legend is a table which shows the symbol and line corresponding to each set of data points (**Figure S3.14**). Since there is only one kind of symbol and one line in this graph, the legend is not needed. Therefore, select [Legend] and choose [None] to remove the default legend. If you choose to keep the legend, you can select where it will be placed on the chart from this same menu.

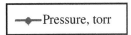

Figure S3.15

8. **Format Axis Scale, decimal places, and other options.** Select [Axes] from the chart layout ribbon and a menu will appear as shown in **Figure S3.16.** Select [Primary horizontal axis] and from that menu select [More Primary horizontal axis options]. A menu as shown in **Figure S3.16** should appear. For the data in this exercise, select the options shown on the right.

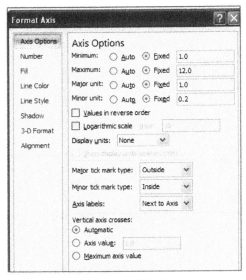

Figure S3.16

Format the y axis scale the same way. Go back to Axis on the Chart Layout ribbon. [Select Primary vertical axis] and then select [More primary vertical axis options]. You will get a menu similar to Fig. 3.14. Complete the Y axis options as follows: Minimum = fixed, 0; Maximum = fixed, 1400; Major unit = fixed, 200; Minor unit = fixed, 50. Major tick mark type: Outside; Minor tick mark type: Inside; Axis labels: Next to axis. Vertical axis crosses: Automatic.

9. **Format the number type:** Select [Number] from the Format Axis menu. From the list of choices select [Number], decimal places 1, and 1000 separator, [none] (you will need to deselect the √ for this (which means there is a comma in the 1000 place (ex. 1,000).

10. Other format axis options: these can be left in the default positions. No need to change them.

11. Add gridlines which make the graph appear like it was made on graph paper. Select Gridlines from the Chart Layout ribbon (**Figure S3.17**). For both Primary horizontal and vertical gridlines, select [Major and Minor Gridlines].

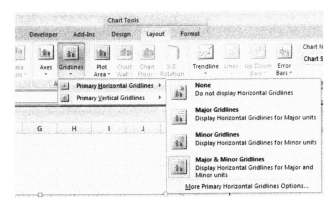

Figure S3.17

12. **Change the color and border of the plot area**. Select ⌈Plot Area⌉ from the Chart Layout ribbon to make changes to the fill inside the plot area or to change the border around the plot area. Select More Plot Area Options to vary the Fill, Border, and Format of the plot area. The sample graph is in the default fill color and border.

13. **More options.** There are many more Excel features that can be used to customize a graph of data. You are encouraged to explore these options as you use computer graphing for this course. For example, some data is best graphed with a **line of best fit**. This can be done by selecting Scatter (without a line) from the Chart ribbon and then Trendline from the Chart Layout ribbon.

14. **Add your name to the graph**. Select the graph by clicking on a blank space. Click on the Insert tab then click on ⌈Header⌉ ⌈& Footer⌉. The Page set-up menu will be displayed (**Figure S3.18**). Select Custom Header and the Header Box will appear. Type your name and any other information the instructor has requested in the ⌈Right section⌉ of the Header box and click OK (twice).

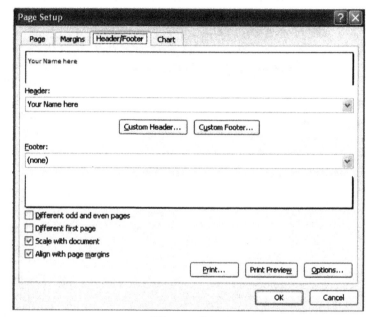

Figure S3.18

15. **Print your graph.** Select the Office icon on the top left corner of the screen. Select Print from the menu and your graph will be printed. Do not close your computer graphing work until your graph is printed in as many copies as you need.

STUDY AID 4

Using a Scientific Calculator

A calculator is useful for most calculations in this book. You should obtain a scientific calculator; that is, one that has at least the following function keys on its keyboard.

Addition $\boxed{+}$ Second function $\boxed{\text{2nd}}$ or $\boxed{\text{INV}}$ or $\boxed{\text{Shift}}$

Subtraction $\boxed{-}$ Change sign $\boxed{+/-}$

Multiplication $\boxed{\times}$ Exponential number $\boxed{\text{Exp}}$

Division $\boxed{\div}$ Logarithm $\boxed{\text{Log}}$

Equals $\boxed{=}$ Antilogarithm $\boxed{10^{\times}}$

Mode $\boxed{\text{MODE}}$

All calculators do not use the same symbolism for these function keys. Not all calculators work the same way. Save the instruction manual that comes with your calculator. It is very useful for determining how to do special operations on your particular model. Refer to your instruction manual for variations from the function symbols shown above and for the use of other function keys.

Some keys have two functions, upper and lower. In order to use the upper (second) function, the second function key $\boxed{\text{2nd}}$ must be pressed in order to activate the desired upper function.

The display area of the calculator shows the numbers entered and often shows more digits in the answer than should be used. The numbers in the display can be in fixed decimal form or in exponential notation, depending on how the calculator is programmed. The MODE key on many calculators is used to change back and forth between fixed decimal and exponential notation. Refer to your instruction manual for how to use this function. Regardless of the digits in the display, the final answer should always be rounded to reflect the proper number of significant figures for the calculations. The calculator will not do that for you.

Addition and Subtraction

To add numbers:

1. Enter the first number to be added followed by the plus key $\boxed{+}$.

2. Enter the second number to be added followed by the plus key $\boxed{+}$.

3. Repeat Step 2 for each additional number to be added, except the last number.

4. After the last number is entered, press the equal key $\boxed{=}$. You should now have the answer in the display area.

5. When a number is to be subtracted, use the minus key $\boxed{-}$ instead of the plus key.

As an example, to calculate 16.0 + 1.223+8.45, enter 16.0 followed by the $\boxed{+}$ key; then enter 1.223 followed by the $\boxed{+}$ key; then enter 8.45 followed by the $\boxed{=}$ key. The display shows 25.673, which is rounded to the answer 25.7.

Examples of Addition and Subtraction

Calculation	Enter in Sequence	Display	Rounded Answer
a. 12.0 + 16.2 + 122.3	12.0 $\boxed{+}$ 16.2 $\boxed{+}$ 122.3 $\boxed{=}$	150.5	150.5
b. 132 − 62 + 141	132 $\boxed{-}$ 62 $\boxed{+}$ 141 $\boxed{=}$	211	211
c. 46.23 + 13.2	46.23 $\boxed{+}$ 13.2 $\boxed{=}$	59.43	59.4
d. 129.06 + 49.1 − 18.3	129.06 $\boxed{+}$ 49.1 $\boxed{-}$ 18.3 $\boxed{=}$	159.86	159.9

Multiplication

To multiply numbers using your calculator

1. Enter the first number to be multiplied followed by the multiplication key $\boxed{\times}$.

2. Enter the second number to be multiplied followed by the multiplication key $\boxed{\times}$.

3. Repeat Step 2 for all other numbers to be multiplied except the last number.

4. Enter the last number to be multiplied followed by the equal key $\boxed{=}$. You now have the answer in the display area. Round off to the proper number of significant figures. As an example, to calculate (3.25)(4.184)(22.2) enter 3.25 followed by the $\boxed{\times}$ key; then enter 4.184 followed by the $\boxed{\times}$ key; then enter 22.2 followed by the $\boxed{=}$ key. The display shows 301.8756, which is rounded to the answer 302.

Examples of Multiplication

Calculation	Enter in Sequence	Display	Rounded Answer
a. (12)(14)(18)	12 $\boxed{\times}$ 14 $\boxed{\times}$ 18 $\boxed{=}$	3024	3.0×10^3
b. (122)(3.4)(60.)	122 $\boxed{\times}$ 3.4 $\boxed{\times}$ 60. $\boxed{=}$	24888	2.5×10^4
c. (0.522)(49.4)(6.33)	0.522 $\boxed{\times}$ 49.4 $\boxed{\times}$ 6.33 $\boxed{=}$	163.23044	163

Division

To divide numbers using your calculator:

1. Enter the numerator followed by the division key $\boxed{\div}$.

2. Enter the denominator followed by the equal key $\boxed{=}$ to give the answer in the display area. Round off to the proper number of significant figures.

3. If there is more than one denominator, enter each denominator followed by the division key except for the last number, which is followed by the equal key. As an example, to calculate $\frac{126}{12}$, enter 126 followed by the $\boxed{\div}$ key; then enter 12 followed by the $\boxed{=}$ key. The display shows 10.5, which is rounded to the answer 11.

Examples of Division

	Calculation	Enter in Sequence	Display	Rounded Answer
a.	$\frac{142}{25}$	142 $\boxed{\div}$ 25 $\boxed{=}$	5.68	5.7
b.	$\frac{0.422}{5.00}$	0.422 $\boxed{\div}$ 5.00 $\boxed{=}$	0.0844	0.0844
c.	$\frac{124}{(0.022)(3.00)}$	124 $\boxed{\div}$ 0.022 $\boxed{\div}$ 3.00 $\boxed{=}$	1878.7878	1.9×10^3

Exponents

In scientific measurements and calculations we often encounter very large and very small numbers. A convenient method of expressing these large and small numbers is by using exponents or powers of 10. A number in exponential form is treated like any other number, that is, it can be added, subtracted, multiplied, or divided.

To enter an exponential number into your calculator first enter the non-exponential part of the number, then press the exponent key $\boxed{\text{Exp}}$, followed by the exponent. For example, to enter 4.94×10^3, enter 4.94, then press $\boxed{\text{Exp}}$, then press 3. When the exponent of 10 is a minus number, press the Change of Sign key $\boxed{+/-}$ after entering the exponent. For example, to enter 4.94×10^{-3}, enter in sequence 4.94 $\boxed{\text{Exp}}$ 3 $\boxed{+/-}$. In most calculators the exponent will appear in the display a couple of spaces after the non-exponent part of the number; for example, 4.94   03 or 4.94   −03.

Examples Using Exponential Numbers

	Calculation	Enter in Sequence	Display	Rounded Answer
a.	$(4.94 \times 10^3)(21.4)$	4.94 $\boxed{\text{Exp}}$ 3 $\boxed{\times}$ 21.4 $\boxed{=}$	105716	1.06×10^5
b.	$(1.42 \times 10^4)(2.88 \times 10^{-5})$	1.42 $\boxed{\text{Exp}}$ 4 $\boxed{\times}$ 2.88 $\boxed{\text{Exp}}$ 5 $\boxed{+/-}$ $\boxed{=}$	0.40896	0.409
c.	$\frac{8.22 \times 10^{-5}}{5.00 \times 10^7}$	8.22 $\boxed{\text{Exp}}$ 5 $\boxed{+/-}$ $\boxed{\div}$ 5.00 $\boxed{\text{Exp}}$ 7 $\boxed{=}$	1.644 −12	1.64×10^{-12}

Logarithms

The logarithm (log) of a number to the base 10 is the power (exponent) to which 10 must be raised to give that number. For example, the log of 100 is 2.0 (log $100 = 10^{2.0}$). The log of 200 is 2.3 (log $200 = 10^{2.3}$). Logarithms are used in chemistry to calculate the pH of an aqueous solution. The answer (log) should contain the same number of significant figures to the right of the decimal as there are significant figures in the original number. Thus the log $100 = 2.0$ but the log 100. is 2.000.

The log key on many calculators is a second function key. To determine the log using your calculator, enter the number, then press the log key $\boxed{\text{Log}}$. For example to determine the log of 125, enter 125, then press the log key $\boxed{\text{Log}}$. The display shows 2.09691, which is rounded to the answer 2.097.

Examples. Determine the log of the following:

Calculation	Enter in Sequence	Display	Rounded Answer
a. log 42	42 $\boxed{\text{Log}}$	1.6232492	1.62
b. log 1.62×10^5	1.62 $\boxed{\text{Exp}}$ 5 $\boxed{\text{Log}}$	5.209515	5.210
c. log 6.4×10^{-6}	6.4 $\boxed{\text{Exp}}$6 $\boxed{+/-}$ $\boxed{\text{Log}}$	−5.19382	−5.19
d. log 2.5	2.5 $\boxed{\text{Log}}$	0.39794	0.40

Antilogarithms (Inverse Logarithms)

An antilogarithm is the number from which the logarithm has been calculated. It is calculated using the to $\boxed{10^\times}$ key on your calculator. Many calculators use the $\boxed{\text{F}}$ or $\boxed{\text{INV}}$ or $\boxed{\text{Shift}}$ key to access this function. To use a function that appears above a key you must first press the $\boxed{\text{F}}$ key. For example, to determine the antilogarithm of 2.891, enter 2.891 into your calculator, then press the $\boxed{\text{F}}$ key followed by the $\boxed{10^\times}$ key. The display shows 778.03655, which is rounded to the answer 778. The answer should contain the same number of figures as there are to the right of the decimal in the antilog. pH can be converted to [H^+] using the $\boxed{10^\times}$ key.

Examples. Determine the antilogarithm of the following:

Calculation	Enter in Sequence	Display	Rounded Answer
a. antilog 1.628	1.628 $\boxed{\text{2nd}}$ $\boxed{10^\times}$	42.461956	42.5
b. antilog 7.086	7.086 $\boxed{\text{2nd}}$ $\boxed{10^\times}$	12189896	1.22×10^7
c. antilog −6.33	6.33 $\boxed{+/-}$ $\boxed{\text{2nd}}$ $\boxed{10^\times}$	4.6773514 −07	4.7×10^{-7}
d. pH 4.5 to [H^+]	4.5 $\boxed{+/-}$ $\boxed{\text{2nd}}$ $\boxed{10^\times}$	3.1622776 −05	3.16×10^{-5}

Additional Practice Problems

Only the problem, the display, and the answers are given.

	Problem	Display	Answer
1.	$143.5 + 14.02 + 1.202$	158.722	158.7
2.	$72.06 - 26.92 - 49.66$	−4.52	−4.52
3.	$2.168 + 4.288 - 1.62$	4.836	4.84
4.	$(12.3)(22.8)(1.235)$	346.3434	346
5.	$(2.42 \times 10^6)(6.08 \times 10^{-4})(0.623)$	916.65728	917
6.	$\dfrac{(46.0)(82.3)}{19.2}$	197.17708	197
7.	$\dfrac{0.0298}{243}$	1.2263374 −04	1.23×10^{-4}
8.	$\dfrac{(5.4)(298)(760)}{(273)(1042)}$	4.2992554	4.3
9.	$(6.22 \times 10^6)(1.45 \times 10^3)(9.00)$	8.1171 10	8.12×10^{10}
10.	$\dfrac{(1.49 \times 10^6)(1.88 \times 10^6)}{6.02 \times 10^{23}}$	4.6531561 −12	4.65×10^{-12}
11.	$\log 245$	2.389166	2.389
12.	$\log 6.5 \times 10^{-6}$	−5.1870866	−5.19
13.	$(\log 24)(\log 34)$	2.1137644	2.11
14.	antilog 6.34	2187761.6	2.2×10^6
15.	antilog −6.34	4.5708819 −07	4.6×10^{-7}

APPENDIX 1

Suggested List of Equipment

Equipment for Student Lockers

1. 5 Beakers: 50, 100, 150, 250, 400 mL
2. 1 Burner, Tirrill (optional)
3. 1 Ceramfab pad
4. 1 Clay triangle
5. 2 Crucibles, size 0
6. 2 Crucible covers, size F
7. 1 Crucible tongs
8. 1 Evaporating dish, size 1
9. 1 File, triangular
10. 1 Filter paper (box)
11. 2 Flasks, Erlenmeyer, 125 mL
12. 2 Flasks, Erlenmeyer, 250 mL
13. 1 Flask, florence, 500 mL
14. 5 Glass plates, 3 × 3 in.
15. 1 Graduated cylinder, 10 mL
16. 1 Graduated cylinder, 50 mL
17. 2 Litmus paper (vials), red and blue
18. 2 Medicine droppers/disposable pipets
19. 1 Pipet, volumetric, 10 mL
20. 8 Rubber stoppers: 3 No. 1, solid; 1 No. 1, 1-hole; 1 No. 4, 1-hole; 1 No. 4, 2-hole; 1 No. 5, solid; 1 No. 6, 2-hole
21. 2 Rubber tubing (about 25 cm), 3/16 in. diameter
22. 1 Screw clamp
23. 1 Spatula
24. 1 Sponge
25. 12 Test tubes, 18 × 150 mm (or culture tubes)
26. 1 Test tube, ignition, 25 × 200 mm
27. 1 Test tube brush
28. 1 Test tube holder, wire
29. 1 Test tube rack
30. 1 Thermometer, 110°C
31. 1 Thistle top, plastic
32. 1 Utility clamp (single buret clamp)
33. 1 Wash bottle (plastic)
34. 2 Watch glasses, 4 in.
35. 5 Wide-mouth bottles, 8 oz.
36. 1 Wing top
37. 1 Wire gauze

Auxillary Equipment Not Supplied in Student Lockers

1. Aluminum foil (7 × 7 cm)
2. Balances
3. Beakers, 600 mL
4. Blender
5. Boyle's law apparatus
6. Büchner funnels, suction flasks, and suction rubber tubing
7. Burets, 25 or 50 mL
8. Buret clamps
9. Burners, Tirrill (if not individually supplied)
10. Capillary Melting point tubes (sealed at one end)
11. Centrifuges
12. Centrifuge tubes
13. Cheese cloth
14. Chromatography columns (polypropylene from Kontes)
15. Deflagration spoons
16. Erlenmeyer flasks, 500 mL
17. Filter paper, Whatman #1 (14 × 14 cm)
18. Filter paper for Büchner funnel
19. Glass rod, 5 or 6 mm
20. Glass tubing, 6 mm
21. Glass wool (pyrex)
22. Glass writing markers
23. Gloves, plastic; small and medium
24. Hair dryers
25. Magnetic stirrers with bars
26. Metric rulers
27. Oil baths
28. pH meters
29. Pipets, graduated, 1 mL, 5 mL, and 10 mL
30. Pipets, micro
31. Pipets, Pasteur
32. Pipets, volumetric; 2 mL and 3 mL
33. Pneumatic troughs
34. Protective rubber gloves
35. Reflux and distillation equipment 100 mL or 200 mL round-bottom distilling flasks Distillation take-off heads Condensers 200° or 250° thermometers 250 mL separatory funnels
36. Ring stands
37. Ring supports, 4 to 5 in. diameter
38. Rubber bands cut from 3/16 inch rubber tubing
39. Spectrophotometers
40. Spray applicators
41. Styrofoam cups, 6 ounce
42. Suction bulbs for pipets
43. Wire stirrers for oil and water baths
44. Four inch cardboard square with a hole for a thermometer
45. See Appendix 3 for special equipment needed for some experiments.
46. See Exp. 8 for special equipment needed.

APPENDIX 2

List of Reagents Required and Preparation of Solutions

Solids

Acetamide, C_2H_5NO

Aluminum foil

Ammonium chloride, NH_4Cl

Barium chloride, $BaCl_2 \cdot 2\,H_2O$

Barium sulfate, $BaSO_4$

Benzoic acid, C_6H_5COOH

Benzophenone, $C_6H_5—CO—C_6H_5$

Benzoyl peroxide, $(C_6H_5COO)_2$

Boiling chips

Candles

Calcium carbide, CaC_2 (small lumps)

Calcium hydroxide, $Ca(OH)_2$

Calcium oxide, CaO

Cholesterol, $C_{27}H_{45}OH$

trans-Cinnamic acid, $C_9H_8O_2$

Copper (II) acetate, $Cu(C_2H_3O_2) \cdot H_2O$, (for Barfoed reagent)

Cobalt chloride paper

Copper strips, Cu

Copper wire, #18, Cu

Copper(II) sulfate pentahydrate, $CuSO_4 \cdot 5\,H_2O$

Cotton

Digitonin, $C_{56}H_{92}O_{29}$

Diphenylacetic acid, $C_{14}H_{12}O_2$

Diphenylacetic acid-cholesterol, 50:50

Dipotassium phosphate, K_2HPO_4, (for phosphate buffer)

Food coloring, red and green paste

Glass wool, pyrex

Glucose, $C_6H_{12}O_6$

Glycine, $C_2H_5NO_2$

Ice

Ice cubes, dark blue

Iodine, I_2

Iron wire (20-24 gauge), Fe

Lead strips, Pb

Lead(II) iodide, PbI_2

Magnesium strips, Mg

Magnesium oxide, MgO

Magnesium sulfate, anhydrous, $MgSO_4$

Magnesium sulfate, $MgSO_4 \cdot 7H_2O$

Manganese dioxide, MnO_2

Marble chips, $CaCO_3$

Marbles, about 20 mm diameter

Menthol, $C_{10}H_{20}O$

Methylene blue, powder

1-Naphthol, (α-naphthol) $C_{10}H_8O$

Ninhydrin, $C_9H_6O_4$

p-Nitroaniline, $C_6H_6N_2O_2$

1-Nitroso-2-naphthol, $C_{10}H_7NO_2$

Orcinol, (3, 5-dihydroxytoluene) $C_7H_8O_2$, (for Bial reagent)

pH indicator paper, 1–14

Phenol, C_6H_5OH

Potassium bicarbonate, $KHCO_3$

Potassium bisulfate, $KHSO_4$

Potassium chlorate, C.P, $KClO_3$

Potassium chloride, C.P, KCl

Potassium hydrogen phthalate, $KHC_8H_4O_4$

Potassium hydroxide, KOH; for phosphate buffer solution

Potato (fresh)

Resorcinol, $C_6H_6O_2$ (for Seliwanoff reagent)

Sand paper or emery cloth

Appendix 2 (continued)

Salicylic acid, $C_6H_4(COOH)(OH)$

Sodium, Na

Sodium bicarbonate, $NaHCO_3$

Sodium carbonate, anhydrous; Na_2CO_3

Sodium chloride (coarse crystals), NaCl

Sodium chloride (fine crystals), NaCl

Sodium Citrate, $C_6H_5Na_3O_2$

Sodium nitrate, $NaNO_3$

Sodium nitrite, $NaNO_2$

Sodium peroxide, Na_2O_2

Sodium potassium tartrate, $NaKC_4H_4O_6$ (used in copper reagent)

Sodium sulfate, anhydrous, Na_2SO_4

Sodium sulfite, Na_2SO_3

Starch, $(C_6H_{10}O_5)_n$

Stearic acid, $CH_3(CH_2)_{16}COOH$

Steel wool, Fe (Grade 0 or 1)

Strontium chloride, $SrCl_2 \cdot 6\, H_2O$

Sucrose, $C_{12}H_{22}O_{11}$

Sulfur, S

Tin (II) chloride, $SnCl_2 \cdot 6H_2O$

Tyrosine, $C_9H_{11}NO_3$

Urea, $(NH_2)_2CO$

Urea-trans-cinnamic acid, 50:50

Vegetable shortening

Wood splints

Xylose, $C_5H_{10}O_5$

Zinc, mossy, Zn

Zinc strips, Zn (0.01 inch thick)

Zinc sulfate, $ZnSO_4 \cdot 7\, H_2O$

Pure Liquids/Commercial Mixtures

Acetic acid (glacial), CH_3COOH

Acetic anhydride, $(CH_3CO)_2O$

Acetone, CH_3COCH_3

Aniline, C_6H_7N

Benzylamine, C_7H_9N

Bromine, Br_2

n-Butyl alcohol (1-butanol), C_4H_9OH

Chloroform, $CHCl_3$

Cyclohexane, C_6H_{12}

Decane, $C_{10}H_{22}$

1,6-Diaminohexane, $C_6H_{16}N_2$

Diethylamine, $C_4H_{11}N$

Ethyl alcohol (ethanol), 95%, C_2H_5OH

Ethyl alcohol, denatured anhydrous

Formaldehyde, formalin, 40% CH_2O solution

Glycerol, $C_3H_5(OH)_3$

Heptane (or low boiling petroleum ether), C_7H_{16}

Hexane, C_6H_{14}

n-Hexylamine, $C_6H_{13}NH_2$

Isoamyl alcohol (3-methyl-1-butanol), $C_5H_{11}OH$

Isopropyl alcohol (2-propanol) C_3H_7OH

Kerosene (alkene free)

Liquid detergent

Methyl alcohol (methanol), CH_3OH

Methyl methacrylate, $CH_2{=}CH(CH_3)COOCH_3$

Mineral oil, (for melting point bath)

Oleic acid, $CH_3(CH_2)_7CH{=}CH(CH_2)_7COOH$

Pentene (amylene), C_5H_{10}

Phosphoric acid, 85% H_3PO_4

Pyridine, C_5H_5N

Red wine

Sulfuric acid, conc., H_2SO_4

Toluene, C_7H_8

1,1,1-Trichloroethane, CCl_3CH_3

Vegetable oils (corn, cottonseed, peanut, soybean, etc.)

Appendix 2 (continued)

Solutions

All solutions, except where otherwise directed, are prepared by dissolving the designated quantity of solute in distilled water and diluting to 1 liter.

Acetic acid, concentrated (glacial), concentrated reagent $HC_2H_3O_2$

Acetic acid, dilute, 6 M; 350 mL concentrated $HC_2H_3O_2$/liter

Acetic acid, 10% solution; 100 mL CH_3COOH + 900 mL H_2O

Acetic acid-1-butanol-water (1:3:1 by volume); 200 mL CH_3COOH + 600 mL C_4H_9OH/liter

Adipoyl chloride, 0.4 M in cyclohexane; 18.3 g adipoyl chloride/250 mL cyclohexane

Alanine, 0.2 M; 1.78 g alanine/100 mL

Alanine·HCl, 0.1 M; 1.26 g alanine·HCl/100 mL

Alanine-aspartic acid-leucine-lysine solution (each 0.2 M); 1.78 g alanine + 2.66 g aspartic acid + 2.62 g leucine + 2.92 g lysine/100 mL

Albumin, 2%; 20 g albumin/liter (Make slurry with about 50 mL water, then add additional water slowly while stirring.)

Aluminum chloride, 0.10 M; 24.1 g $AlCl_3$·6 H_2O/liter

Ammonium chloride, 0.1 M; 5.4 g NH_4Cl/liter

Ammonium chloride, saturated; 410 g NH_4Cl/liter

Ammonium hydroxide, concentrated; concentrated reagent, NH_4OH

Ammonium hydroxide, dilute, 6 M; 400 mL concentrated/liter, NH_4OH

Arabinose, 1%; 10 g arabinose/liter

Arginine-tyrosine solution (each 0.1 %); 100 mg arginine + 100 mg tyrosine/100 mL pH 6.0 phosphate buffer

Arsenomolybdate reagent; Nelson's arsenomolybdate reagent is commercially available from Sigma Chemical Co., St. Louis, Missouri

Aspartic acid, 0.2 M; 2.66 g aspartic acid/100 mL

Barfoed reagent; dissolve 13.3 g $Cu(C_2H_3O_2)_2$·H_2O in 200 mL H_2O. (Filter if necessary), add 1.8 mL $HC_2H_3O_2$ (glacial). Copper(II) acetate is slow to dissolve.

Barium chloride, 0.10 M; 24.4 g $BaCl_2$·2 H_2O/liter

Barium hydroxide, saturated; 10 g $Ba(OH)_2$·8 H_2O/100 mL

Barium hydroxide, 0.2 M; 15.8 g $Ba(OH)_2$·8 H_2O/250 mL

Benedict reagent; dissolve 86.5 g sodium citrate and 50 g anhydrous Na_2CO_3 in 400 mL water with heating. Dissolve 8.65 g $CuSO_4$·5 H_2O in 50 mL water. Mix these two solutions slowly and add water to produce 500 mL of solution.

Bial reagent; dissolve 1.5 g orcinol (3, 5-dihydroxytoluene) in 500 mL conc. HCl and add 1.5 mL of 10% aqueous $FeCl_3$

Bleach, 10% NaOCl solution

Blood, sheep (or any mammalian non-human blood) Should be fresh. (Ward's Scientific or Carolina Biological Supply, or local source).

Bromine in 1,1,1-trichloroethane, 5% solution; 2.5 mL Br_2 plus 100 mL CCl_3CH_3

Buffer solution, standard pH 4.0, 7.0, 10.0; commercially available

Calcium chloride, 0.1 M; 14.7 g $CaCl_2 \cdot 2\ H_2O$/liter

Chlorine water; dilute 150 mL of 5.25% NaOCl (household bleach) to 1 liter. Add 15 mL concentrated HCl and mix gently.

Cholesterol standard solution; $C_{27}H_{45}OH$ (dissolve 120 mg cholesterol in 60 mL isopropyl alcohol)

Cobalt (II) chloride, 0.1 M; 23.8 g $CoCl_2 \cdot 6\ H_2O$/liter

Copper (II) nitrate, 0.1 M; 24.2 g $Cu(NO_3)_2 \cdot 3\ H_2O$/liter

Copper reagent; dissolve 24 g of anhydrous Na_2CO_3, 16 g of sodium potassium tartrate, 4 g of $CuSO_4 \cdot 5\ H_2O$, and 180 g of anhydrous Na_2SO_4 in water and dilute to 1 liter.

Copper(II) sulfate, 0.1 M; 25.0 g $CuSO_4 \cdot 5\ H_2O$/liter; or dilute 0.2 M with an equal volume of water

Copper(II) sulfate, 0.2 M; 50.0 g $CuSO_4 \cdot 5\ H_2O$/liter

Copper (II) sulfate, 1%; 1 g $CuSO_4 \cdot 5\ H_2O$ + 99 mL H_2O

Cysteine·HCl, 0.10 M; 1.56 g cysteine·HCl/100 mL

1,6-Diaminohexane (Hexamethylenediamine), 0.40 M in 0.40 M NaOH; dissolve 11.6 g $(CH_2)_6(NH_2)_2$/250 mL 0.4 M NaOH

Digitonin solution; dissolve 1.0 g digitonin in 50 mL ethanol

Dowex-50 slurry; The resin must be in the H^+ form. Newly purchased resin or used resin is washed sequentially with deionized water, acetone (use only for the new resin), 1 M NaOH, deionized water, 1 M HCl, and deionized water. The washed resin is suspended in the pH 6 phosphate buffer two or three times or until the slurry has a pH of 6. Store the slurry in the cold.

Ethanol-Acetone (1:1 by volume); 500 mL CH_3CH_2OH + 500 mL CH_3COCH_3

Ethanol, denatured, CH_3CH_2OH

Ethanol/water, 500 mL CH_3CH_2OH + 500 mL H_2O

Food colors, blue, green, and yellow; commercially available products

Formaldehyde, 10% solution; 25 mL formalin (40% CH_2O) plus 75 mL H_2O

Fructose, 1% solution; 1.0 g fructose/100 mL

Fruit juices; orange, lemon, lime, grapefruit, apple, etc. (fresh if available)

Gelatin, 2% solution; 10 g gelatin/500 mL (Dissolves slowly)

Glucose, 0.020 M; 3.6 g $C_6H_{12}O_6$/liter

Glucose, 1% solution; 5 g $C_6H_{12}O_6$/500 mL H_2O

Glucose, 10% solution; 10 g $C_6H_{12}O_6$ plus 90 mL H_2O

Glucose, standard solutions; made up to contain 2.0, 5.0, 8.0, 12.0, 15.0, and 18 mg glucose/100 mL solution

Glutamic acid·HCl, 0.10 M; 1.84 g glutamic acid·HCl/100 mL

Glycine·HCl, 0.10 M; 1.40 g glycine·HCl/100 mL

Glycine, 1% solution; 1.0 g glycine/100 mL

Histidine·HCl, 0.10 M; 2.10 g histidine·HCl/100 mL

Hydrochloric acid, concentrated, concentrated reagent, HCl

Hydrochloric acid, 0.020 M, 6.7 mL of 3.0 M HCL/liter

Hydrochloric acid, 1.0 M; 86 mL conc. HCL/liter

Hydrochloric acid, dilute, 3 M; 250 mL concentrated HCl/liter

Hydrochloric acid, dilute, 6 M; 500 mL concentrated HCl/liter

Hydrochloric acid, 0.1 M; 8.33 mL concentrated acid HCl/liter; (or dilute 10 mL of 6 M HCl to 600 mL)

Hydrochloric acid, 0.01 M; 0.83 mL concentrated acid HCl/liter; (or dilute 10 mL of 0.1 M HCl to 100 mL)

Hydrochloric acid, 0.001 M; 0.083 mL concentrated acid HCl/liter; (or dilute 10 mL 0.1 M to 1000 mL)

Hydrogen peroxide, 3%; reagent solution or 100 mL 30% H_2O_2/liter

Hydrogen peroxide, 6%; 200 mL 30% H_2O_2/liter; store cold (handle 30% with gloves)

Hydrogen peroxide, 9%; 300 mL 30% H_2O_2/liter; store cold

Hydrogen peroxide, 30% H_2O_2 (for dilution); store cold (handle with gloves)

Iodine, 0.020 M in KI; 1.5 g KI per 100 mL water, add 0.51 g I_2

Iodine in potassium iodide, 1%; 10 g I_2 + 20 g KI/liter (Dissolve I_2 and KI in about 50 mL H_2O, then dilute to 1 liter)

Iodine water, saturated; 5 g I_2/liter

Iron (III) chloride, 0.1 M; 27.1 g $FeCl_3$·6 H_2O + 5 mL concentrated HCl/liter

Iron reagent; 2.5 g $FeCl_3$·6 H_2O/100 mL phosphoric acid

Isopropyl alcohol-water (2:1 by volume); 667 mL $CH_3CH(OH)CH_3$/liter

Lead (II) acetate, 0.1 M; 3.25 g $Pb(C_2H_3O_2)_2$/100 mL

Lead (II) nitrate, 0.10 M; 33.1 g $Pb(NO_3)_2$/liter

Leucine, 0.2 M; 2.62 g leucine/100 mL

Lysine, 0.2 M; 2.92 g lysine/100 mL

Lysine·HCl, 0.1 M; 1.83 g lysine·HCl/100 mL

Magnesium sulfate, 0.1 M; 24.6 g $MgSO_4$·7 H_2O/liter

Maltose, 1% solution; 5.0 g maltose/500 mL

Milk, fat free (skim)

Molisch reagent; dissolve 2.5 g α-naphthol in 50 mL 95% C_2H_5OH

Nickel nitrate, 0.1 M; 29.1 g $Ni(NO_3)_2 \cdot 6\ H_2O$/liter

Ninhydrin, 0.3%; 1.5 g ninhydrin/500 mL acetone

Ninhydrin, 0.2%; dissolve 0.2 g of ninhydrin in 100 mL of 1-butanol which is saturated with water

Nitric acid, concentrated; concentrated reagent, HNO_3

Nitric acid, dilute, 3 M; 188 mL concentrated HNO_3/liter

Nitric acid, dilute, 6 M; 375 mL concentrated HNO_3/liter

1-Nitroso-2-naphthol, 0.1 % in acetone, $C_{10}H_7NO_2$; dissolve 0.17 g in 100 mL acetone

Phenol, 1% solution; 5.0 g C_6H_5OH/500 mL

Phenolphthalein, 0.2% solution; dissolve 2 g phenolphthalein in 600 mL ethanol (95%) and dilute with water to 1 liter

Phosphate buffer, 0.2 M; 34.8 g K_2HPO_4/liter and adjust pH to 6.0 using a pH meter and dilute H_3PO_4 or KOH solution

Phosphoric acid, 85% reagent, H_3PO_4

Phosphoric acid, dilute, 3 M; 201 mL 85% H_3PO_4 solution/liter

Potassium chloride, saturated; 390 g KCl/liter

Potassium nitrate, 0.1 M; 10.1 g KNO_3/liter

Potassium permanganate, 0.1 M; 15.8 g $KMnO_4$/liter

Potassium permanganate, 0.002 M; 0.16 g $KMnO_4$/500 mL H_2O

Potassium thiocyanate, 0.1 M; 9.7 g KSCN/liter

Seliwanoff reagent; dissolve 0.50 g resorcinol in 1000 mL 4 M HCl (333 mL conc. HCl diluted to 1000 mL)

Silver nitrate, 0.10 M; 17.0 g $AgNO_3$/liter

Sodium bicarbonate, 5% solution; 50 g $NaHCO_3$/liter

Sodium bicarbonate, saturated solution; 125 g $NaHCO_3$/liter

Sodium bromide, 0.1 M; 10.3 g NaBr/liter

Sodium carbonate, 0.020 M, 2.1 g Na_2CO_3/liter

Sodium carbonate, 0.1 M; 10.6 g Na_2CO_3/liter

Sodium chloride, 0.020 M, 1.2 g NaCl/liter

Sodium chloride, 0.1 M; 5.85 g NaCl/liter

Sodium chloride, saturated; 60 g NaCl/liter

Sodium hydroxide, 0.020 M, 0.80 g NaOH/liter

Sodium hydroxide, 1.25 M; 50. g NaOH/liter

Sodium hydroxide, 10% solution; 111 g NaOH/liter

Sodium hydroxide, 1% solution; 11.1 g NaOH/liter

Sodium hydroxide, 0.1 M; 4 g NaOH/liter

Sodium hydroxide, 1.25 M, 50. g NaOH/liter

Sodium hydroxide, 0.4 M; 16 g NaOH/liter

Sodium iodide, 0.1 M; 15.0 g NaI/liter

Sodium nitrite, 0.1 M; 6.9 g $NaNO_2$/liter

Sodium phosphate, 0.1 M; 38.0 g $Na_3PO_4 \cdot 12\ H_2O$/liter

Sodium sulfate, 0.1 M; 14.2 g Na_2SO_4/liter

Starch, 1 % solution; 5 g/500 mL (Make slurry and disperse in hot water.)

Sucrose, 1% solution; 10 g sucrose ($C_{12}H_{22}O_{11}$)/liter (freshly prepared)

Sulfuric acid, concentrated; concentrated reagent H_2SO_4

Sulfuric acid, dilute, 9 M; carefully, with stirring, slowly add 500 mL concentrated H_2SO_4 to 400 mL H_2O, cool and dilute to 1 liter

Sulfuric acid, dilute, 3 M; 167 mL concentrated H_2SO_4/liter

Vinegar, commercial (colorless), $HC_2H_3O_2$

Wine, commercial red

Xylose, 1% solution; 1.0 g xylose/100 mL

Zinc nitrate, 0.1 M; 29.8 g $Zn(NO_3)_2 \cdot 6\ H_2O$/liter

Zinc sulfate, 0.2 M; 14.4 g $ZnSO_4 \cdot 7\ H_2O$/250 mL

APPENDIX 3

Special Equipment or Preparations Needed

Experiment 1. Laboratory Techniques

A small sample of solid lead(II) iodide and sodium nitrate are needed for comparison purposes only.

Experiment 2. Measurements

An assortment of metal slugs or other solid objects are needed as unknowns for density determination. The diameter of the slugs should be such that they will fit into the 50 mL graduated cylinder. Suggested materials are aluminum, brass, magnesium, steel, etc. Slugs should be numbered for identification.

Experiment 3. Preparation and Properties of Oxygen

Three demonstrations are suggested (see experiment for details). Büchner funnel-vacuum flask setup for disposal of waste MnO_2.

Experiment 4. Preparation and Properties of Hydrogen

For safety: Instructor should dispense sodium metal (size of pieces should be no larger than a 4 mm cube).

Experiment 5. Calorimetry and Specific Heat

An assortment of metal objects like those used for the density determinations in Exp. 2 are needed. They must be small enough to fit into the test tube with id = 22 mm. Styrofoam cups and cardboard cut into 4" squares with a small thermometer hole in the middle should also be available.

Experiment 6. Freezing Points—Graphing of Data

Slotted corks or stoppers, crushed ice

Experiment 7. Water in Hydrates

An assortment of samples for unknowns for determination of percent water is needed. Samples can be issued in small coin envelopes or plastic vials. See the Instructor's Manual for the suggested list of samples.

Experiment 8. Water, Solutions, and pH

The dark blue ice cubes are made by adding methylene blue to tap water until the color is a deep blue. The resulting solution is then frozen in an ice cube tray (Station A6). The green and red colored water is made by adding the food coloring paste to tap water until the resulting solution is brightly colored (Station A4). Much more red water will be needed than green water. The five lengths of capillary tubing needed should have inner diameter measurements that are different depending on what is available. Example: five tubes with i.d. from among the following: 1.0 mm, 1.5 mm, 2.0 mm, 2.5 mm, 3.0 mm, 3.5 mm; or 0.5 mm, 1.0mm, 1.25 mm, 1.75 mm, 2.75 mm; small electric table fan, 1000 mL beaker or battery jar; micropipettes (Pipetman), 200 μL and 1000 μL with disposable tips.

A series of stations is set up for Sections A1-7 and B 3 #6 instead of each student setting up each activity separately at their own lab bench. A station for measuring pH with a pH meter (B3 #6) is recommended. The other B sections of the experiment can be completed by all students at their own place on the bench. The stations needed are:

Station #	Title of the Experiment/ Observation	Materials needed
Station Al	Molecular Structure & Polarity of Water	Ball and stick molecular model kits (2 or 3 should suffice)
Station A2	Polarity of water and Hydrogen Bonds Between Water Molecules	Buret filled with water, 250 mL beaker, plastic rod (even a smooth plastic ruler will work) and soft rayon or silk cloth.
Station A3	Cohesion and Surface Tension	Clean glass microscope slides, dropping bottles of distilled water and 95% ethanol, and liquid detergent; culture dishes, forceps, common pins
Station A4	Capillarity, Cohesion and Adhesion	5 in. pieces of glass capillary tubing with increasing i.d. measurements taped to a white index card with at least 1 inch of the tubes extending beyond the bottom edge of the card; a shallow dish of green water, metric rulers.
Station A5 #1-5	Specific Heat (may want to provide three or four of this station since it takes more time than the other activities)	Two 250. mL Erlenmeyer flasks w/2-hole rubber stoppers inserted; thermometers inserted into one hole; large hot plate; two 600 mL beakers
Station A5, #6	Heat of Vaporization	Two thermometers, riag stand, buret clamp, cotton or rayon tubing to cover the thermometer bulbs; table fan
Station A6.	Water Temperature and Density	1000 mL beaker or battery jar, warm tap water, cold red tap water (pre-mixed, refrigerated to 4°C) 10 mL graduated pipet, pipet pump, blue ice cubes, tongs or gloves

(continued)

Station A7.	Density and volume	Electronic balance with at least 0.001 g precision, weigh boats (1"), micropipettes (Pipetman, 200 μL and 1000 μL), disposable pipet tips
Station B 3 #6	Measurement of pH using a pH Meter	Several pH meters so several students can measure pH for these solutions at the same time. If students are unfamiliar with the use of a pH meter, a card with instructions for use should be with each instrument

Experiment 13.   Ionization—Electrolytes and pH

Conductivity apparatus is needed for the demonstration. The procedure is based on the apparatus described in the experiment but other types may be used without detracting from the results of the demonstration. A magnetic stirrer greatly facilitates the last part of the demonstrations. Two or three pH meters are recommended for student use, set up at stations with the solutions described in the experiment.

Experiment 14.   Identification of Selective Anions

Two unknown solutions (in test tubes) are to be issued to each student. Stock reagents used in the experiment are satisfactory for unknowns. See Instructor's Manual for details.

Experiment 16.   Electromagnetic Energy and Spectroscopy

Hand-held spectroscopes, 1.75 m springs for simulating wave motion (1 per 5 students), vapor lamps with power supplies (2 hydrogen and 2 neon); spectrum chart, incandescent and fluorescent lights, spectrophotometers with range from 350-700 nm, colored pencils, meter sticks, stopwatches (recommended). See Instructor's Manual for more details.

Experiment 17.   Lewis Structures and Molecular Models

Ball-and-stick molecular model sets. Two students can share one kit. The number of sets required depends on how many labs are run simultaneously. It is also possible to purchase a large class set of components and divide them into smaller custom kits.

Experiment 18.   Boyle's Law

Boyle's law apparatus is needed. The kits for this experiment can be purchased from several vendors as "Simple Form Boyle's Law Apparatus" or "Elasticity of Gases Kit." The kits include the silicone grease but not the applied weights and vernier calipers. Slotted masses of 0.5 kg and 1 kg allow the applied weights to lie flat on the platform. If not enough slotted masses are available, a combination of bricks and slotted masses works well. One balance per laboratory with the capacity for weighing the heaviest mass to three significant figures. All masses can be preweighed and labeled with tape displaying their mass.

Appendix 3 (continued)

Experiment 20.   Liquids—Vapor Pressure and Boiling Points

125 mL flasks containing acetone, methanol, ethanol, and water are needed for Part A. It is suggested that students work in pairs in Part B. A 1-gallon metal can is needed for the demonstration in Part C.

Experiment 21.   Molar Volume of a Gas

A 3.0 cc or 5.0 cc disposable syringe is needed for each setup. Needle-rubber stopper assemblies that contain a rubber stopper and syringe needle should be preassembled and checked out and in by students. An additional safety feature is to snip off the end of the needle with a wire cutter after it is in the stopper. The needles need to be heavy enough to push through a rubber stopper without bending. 2 L beakers or battery jars. Büchner funnel-vacuum flask setup needed for disposal of MnO_2.

Experiment 22.   Neutralization—Titration I

The following are needed by each student: A small vial or test tube containing about 4 grams of potassium hydrogen phthalate (KHP) (these vials are collected for reuse), one 25 or 50 mL buret, a buret clamp, and 250 mL of unknown NaOH molarity. The NaOH solution is used in Experiments 22 and 23. See Instructor's Manual for details.

Experiment 23.   Neutralization—Titration II

The following are needed by each student: A 10 mL volumetric pipet, one 25 or 50 mL buret, 50 mL of acid solution of unknown molarity, 50 mL of vinegar, and 125 mL of standard NaOH solution if Experiment 22 is not done. See Instructor's Manual for details.

Experiment 25.   Heat of Reaction

Styrofoam cups are needed.

Experiment 26.   Distillation of Volatile Liquids

Distillation setup using a 125 mL or 250 mL flask (see Figure 26.1); hot plates or heating mantles (with rheostats). Red wine as the alcoholic beverage for distillation. Pot holders or mitts to handle hot plate.

Experiment 27.   Boiling Points and Melting Points

Boiling point and melting point apparatus (see experiment for details), 200°–250°C thermometers, wire stirrers, capillary melting point tubes, and unknown solids are required. See Instructor's Manual for details.

Experiment 28.   Hydrocarbons

Lumps of calcium carbide are needed. Test kerosene to see if it is free of alkenes. Toluene is *not* reacted with bromine.

Experiment 29.   Alcohols, Esters, Aldehydes, and Ketones

Furnish No. 18 copper wire with five or six spiral turns at one end. Wire should be about 20 cm overall in length.

Experiment 30.   Esterification—Distillation: Synthesis of n-Butyl Acetate

This is a two laboratory period experiment. Reflux and distillation equipment (see experiment for details), 200°–250°C thermometer, and 250 mL separatory funnel are required. If available, a heat source without open flame such as a hot plate or heating mantle with rheostat is recommended. See Experiment 26 for this setup.

Experiment 31.   Synthesis of Aspirin

Büchner funnel, suction flask, suction tubing, melting point apparatus, and capillary melting point tubes are needed.

Experiment 32.   Amines and Amides

An ice bath is needed to cool the dye reaction.

Experiment 33.   Polymers—Macromolecules

Benzoyl peroxide is a shock and heat sensitive material. It should be dispensed to each student by the instructor or by qualified stock room personnel.

Experiment 34.   Carbohydrates

Pure fresh or frozen fruit juices, such as orange, lemon, lime, grapefruit, and apple are needed.

Experiment 35.   Glucose Concentration in Sheep Blood

Spectrophotometer, 10 mL graduated pipets, 20 mm diameter marbles, protective gloves, and sheep blood are needed. Safe handling of all blood and body fluids must be stressed.

Experiment 37.   Paper Chromatography

Five hundred mL Erlenmeyer flasks, 14 × 14 cm squares Whatman No. 1 filter paper, 7 × 7 cm squares of Al foil, hair dryer, micropipets and a spray applicator for ninhydrin are needed. An unknown amino acid or amino acid mixture is required for each student.

Appendix 3 (continued)

Experiment 38.   Ion-Exchange Chromatography

Chromatography columns (see experiment for details), Dowex-50 resin slurry, and 600 mL beakers must be provided.

Experiment 39.   Identification of an Unknown Amino Acid by Titration

pH meter, pH 7.0 buffer, and magnetic stirrer are needed. An unknown amino acid is issued to each student or student pair.

Experiment 40.   Enzymatic Catalysis—Catalase

A potato is needed for each student or student pair. A blender is needed to homogenize the potato/water mixture for preparation of catalase. Büchner funnel filtering setup; cheese cloth.

Experiment 42.   Cholesterol Levels in Sheep Blood

Sheep blood, spectrophotometer, centrifuge, centrifuge tubes, 1 mL and 5 mL graduated pipets, and protective gloves are needed. Safe handling of all blood and body fluids should be stressed.

APPENDIX 4

Units of Measurements

Numerical Value of Prefixes with Units

Prefix	Symbol	Number	Power of 10
mega	M	1,000,000	1×10^6
kilo	k	1,000	1×10^3
hecto	h	100	1×10^2
deca	da	10	1×10^1
deci	d	0.1	1×10^{-1}
centi	c	0.01	1×10^{-2}
milli	m	0.001	1×10^{-3}
micro	μ	0.000001	1×10^{-6}
nano	n	0.000000001	1×10^{-9}

Conversion of Units

1 m	=	1000 mm
1 cm	=	10 mm
2.54 cm	=	1 in.
453.6 g	=	1 lb
1 kg	=	2.2 lb, 1000 g
1 g	=	1000 mg
1 L	=	1000 mL
1 mL	=	1 cm^3
0.946 L	=	1 qt
1 cal	=	4.184 J
1 Torr	=	1 mm Hg
760 torr	=	1 atm

Metric Abbreviations

meter	m
centimeter	cm
millimeter	mm
nanometer	nm
liter	L
milliliter	mL
kilogram	kg
gram	g
milligram	mg
mole	mol

Temperature Conversion Formulas

$$°C = \frac{(°F - 32)}{1.8}$$

$$°F = 1.8 \, °C + 32$$

$$K = °C + 273$$

APPENDIX 5

Solubility Table

	$C_2H_3O_2^-$	AsO_4^{3-}	Br^-	CO_3^{2-}	Cl^-	CrO_4^{2-}	OH^-	I^-	NO_3^-	$C_2O_4^{2-}$	O^{2-}	PO_4^{3-}	SO_4^{2-}	S^{2-}	SO_3^{2-}
Al^{3+}	aq	I	aq	–	aq	–	I	aq	aq	–	I	I	aq	d	–
NH_4^+	aq	aq	aq	aq	aq	aq	aq	aq	aq	aq	–	aq	aq	aq	aq
Ba^{2+}	aq	I	aq	I	aq	I	sl. aq	aq	aq	I	sl. aq	I	I	d	I
Bi^{3+}	–	sl. aq	d	I	d	–	I	I	d	I	I	sl. aq	d	I	–
Ca^{2+}	aq	I	aq	I	aq	aq	I	aq	aq	I	I	I	I	d	I
Co^{2+}	aq	I	aq	I	aq	I	I	aq	aq	I	I	I	aq	I	I
Cu^{2+}	aq	I	aq	I	aq	I	I	–	aq	I	I	I	aq	I	–
Fe^{2+}	aq	I	aq	sl. aq	aq	–	I	aq	aq	I	I	I	aq	I	sl. aq
Fe^{3+}	I	I	aq	I	aq	I	I	–	aq	aq	I	I	aq	I	–
Pb^{2+}	aq	I	I	I	I	I	I	I	aq	I	I	I	I	I	I
Mg^{2+}	aq	d	aq	I	aq	aq	I	aq	aq	I	I	I	aq	d	sl. aq
Hg_2^{2+}	sl. aq	I	I	I	I	sl. aq	–	I	aq	I	I	I	I	I	–
Hg^{2+}	aq	I	I	I	aq	sl. aq	I	I	aq	I	I	I	d	I	–
K^+	aq	aq	aq	aq	aq	aq	aq	aq	aq	aq	aq	aq	aq	aq	aq
Ag^+	sl. aq	I	I	I	I	I	–	I	aq	I	I	I	I	I	I
Na^+	aq	aq	aq	aq	aq	aq	aq	aq	aq	aq	aq	aq	aq	aq	aq
Zn^{2+}	aq	I	aq	I	aq	I	I	aq	aq	I	I	I	aq	I	I

Key: aq = Soluble in water   I = Insoluble in water (less than 1 g/100 g H_2O)
      sl. aq = Slightly soluble in water   d = Decomposes in water

APPENDIX 6

Vapor Pressure of Water

Temperature (°C)	Vapor Pressure torr (or mm Hg)	Temperature (°C)	Vapor Pressure torr (or mm Hg)
0	4.6	26	25.2
5	6.5	27	26.7
10	9.2	28	28.3
15	12.8	29	30.0
16	13.6	30	31.8
17	14.5	40	55.3
18	15.5	50	92.5
19	16.5	60	149.4
20	17.5	70	233.7
21	18.6	80	355.1
22	19.8	90	525.8
23	21.2	100	760.0
24	22.4	110	1074.6
25	23.8		

APPENDIX 7

Boiling Points of Liquids

Liquid	Boiling Point °C
Acetone	56.5
Ethanol	78.4
Diethyl ether	34.6
Methanol	64.7
1-propanol	82.5
Water	100.0

APPENDIX 6

Vapor Pressure of Water

Temperature (°C)	Vapor Pressure torr (or mm Hg)	Temperature (°C)	Vapor Pressure torr (or mm Hg)
0	4.6	26	25.2
5	6.5	27	26.7
10	9.2	28	28.3
15	12.8	29	30.0
16	13.6	30	31.8
17	14.5	40	55.3
18	15.5	50	92.5
19	16.5	60	149.4
20	17.5	70	233.7
21	18.6	80	355.1
22	19.8	90	525.8
23	21.2	100	760.0
24	22.4	110	1074.6
25	23.8		

APPENDIX 7

Boiling Points of Liquids

Liquid	Boiling Point °C
Acetone	56.5
Ethanol	78.4
Diethyl ether	34.6
Methanol	64.7
1-propanol	82.5
Water	100.0

APPENDIX 8

Waste Disposal Requirements for Each Experiment

Listed below are special waste containers specified in the experiments for student disposal of waste. Where students are instructed to dispose of wastes in the sink, or where the experiment does not generate waste, the requirements are listed as NONE.

We use the same Waste Heavy Metal bottle for many experiments by combining all the ions poured into it on the label. The same can be done for Organic Solvent Waste bottles.

Exp	Title	Waste Containers That Should Be Available to Students	
1	Laboratory Techniques	Waste Heavy Metals (Pb^+)	bottle
		Waste PbI_2 on filter paper	jar
		Waste or broken glass	Container
2	Measurements	None	
3	Prep. and Prop. of Oxygen	Recycled 9% H_2O_2, unreacted	bottle
		Büchner funnel-vacuum flask	
		for disposal of waste MnO_2	jar
4	Prep. and Prop. of Hydrogen	Recycled Mossy Zinc, rinsed	jar
		unreacted metal strips	jar
5	Calorimetery and Specific Heat	None	
6	Freezing Points	Waste Acetic/Benzoic Acid Mixture	bottle
7	Water in Hydrates	Waste Heavy Metal Residues (Cu^{2+}, Zn^{2+}, Sr^{2+}, Ba^{2+})	jar
8	Water, Solutions and pH.	Waste Organic Solvents (decane)	bottle
9	Properties of Solutions	Waste Organic Solvent (decane)	bottle
		Waste Kerosene Mixtures	bottle
		Waste Heavy Metal Solutions (Ba^{2+})	bottle
10	Composition of Potassium Chlorate	Waste Heavy Metals (Ag^+)	bottle
		Unused $KClO_3$	bottle
11	Double Displacement Reactions	Waste Heavy Metals (Ag^+, Ba^{2+}, Cu^{2+}, Zn^{2+})	bottle

Exp	Title	Waste Containers That Should Be Available to Students	
12	Single Displacement Reactions	Waste Heavy Metals (Ag^+, Cu^{2+}, Pb^{2+}, Zn^{2+})	bottle
13	Ionization—Electrolytes and pH	None (Students do not handle the heavy metal solutions in the demonstration.)	
14	Identification of Selected Anions	Waste Organic Solvents (decane) Waste Heavy Metals (Ag^+, Ba^{2+})	bottle bottle
15	Quantitative Preparation of KCl	None	
16	EM Energy and Spectroscopy	Waste Heavy Metals (Ni^{2+}, MnO_4^-)	bottle
17	Lewis Structures/Molecular Models	None	
18	Boyle's Law	None	
19	Charles' Law	None	
20	Liquids—Vapor Pressure and Boiling Points	None	
21	Molar Volume of a Gas	Büchner funnel-vacuum flask for disposal of the MnO_2 and filter paper. Waste basket	
22	Neutralization—Titration I	None	
23	Neutralization—Titration II	None	
24	Chemical Equilibrium	Waste Heavy Metals (Ag^+, Co^{2+}, Cu^{2+})	bottle
25	Heat of Reaction	None	
26	Distillation of Volatile Liquids	Recycled Ethanol/Ethanol Distillate	bottle
27	Boiling Points and Melting Points	Waste Organic Solvents Used melting point tubes	bottle jar
28	Hydrocarbons	Waste Organic Solvents Waste Heavy Metals (Ag)	bottle bottle

Exp	Title	Waste Containers That Should Be Available to Students	
29	Alcohols, Esters, Aldehydes, Ketones	Waste Organic Solvents	bottle
		Waste Heavy metals (MnO_4^- Ag^+)	bottle
30	Esterification—Distillation	Waste Organic Solvents	bottle
		Solid wastes	jar
31	Synthesis of Aspirin	none	
32	Amines and Amides	Waste Organic Solvents	bottle
33	Polymers—Macromolecules	Waste Organic Solvents	bottle
		Solid waste (nylon and Lucite)	jar
34	Carbohydrates	Molisch test	bottle
		Seliwanoff test	bottle
		Benedict and Barfoed tests	bottle
		Bial test	bottle
		Dehydration (carbon)	jar
35	Glucose Concentration in Blood	Filter paper waste	jar
		Arsenic waste	bottle
36	Amino Acids and Proteins	Biuret test (Cu^{2+})	bottle
		Tyrosine and Ninhydrin tests	bottle
		Waste heavy metals (Pb^{2+})	bottle
		Solid wastes	jar
37	Paper Chromatography	Waste Organic Solvents	bottle
		Solid waste	jar
38	Ion-Exchange Chromatography	Waste Organic Solvents	bottle
		Used resin (for recycling)	jar
39	Unknown Amino Acid by Titration	none	
40	Enzyme Catalysis—Catalase	none	
41	Lipids	Waste Organic Solvents	bottle
		Solid wastes	jar
42	Cholesterol Level in Blood	RBC solids	jar